D1614456

CLOCKS AND THEIR VALUE

CLOCKS AND THEIR VALUE

Illustrated guide to ancient and modern clocks with a unique chart of all known Tompion clocks

by

Donald de Carle, F.B.H.I.

N.A.G Press Ltd., London W.C.1.

First edition 1968

By the same author:—
With the Watchmaker at the Bench.
British Time
Practical Watch Repairing.
Practical Clock Repairing.
The Watchmakers Lathe.
Complicated Watches and Their Repair.
Clock and Watch Repairing.
Clock and Watch Encyclopaedia.
Practical Watch Adjusting and Springing.
Horology.

7198 0010 2

Printed by W. & G. Baird, Ltd., Belfast
and bound by Dorstel Press Ltd., Harlow

Preface

From literally thousands of clocks of different nationalities, periods, construction and design, the clocks enumerated and illustrated in this book are, I believe, representative.

With many of the examples illustrated and described there are numerous specimens available of varying design, but basically the clock illustrated or described is a fair or average specimen, and will form a good picture of that particular type of clock.

The dates of clocks given are, and can only be, approximate, say 10 to 15 years either way. In some instances a precise date can be established such as by the date of a patent.

Generally speaking one period overlaps another and maybe a particular style will outlive the normal period, as for instance the lantern clock.

While the greatest care has been taken in preparing this book, errors may have crept in, but I feel sure there are no major discrepancies but of course there may be omissions.

The values given can only be approximate: so much depends upon the quality of a clock in its entirety, and its genuineness, particularly antique clocks.

If the reader is fortunate it may be possible to procure a clock at 50% or more than 50% less than the estimated values quoted. In other words, there is no definite market value for antique and second-hand clocks, but the values quoted do, it is hoped, form a guide.

It must be borne in mind that the values quoted are for genuine examples which are in first class condition, both as regards the movement and the case. I am conscious that to give values can be dangerous and debatable but even so, it adds interest. The values quoted are given after careful consideration.

Collecting clocks, whether antique or second-hand, is an interesting hobby, and it can be remunerative.

There is scope for the person with a few pounds to spend as well as for the wealthy.

When anticipating spending a large sum, maybe hundreds or even thousands, it is most advisable to seek the advice of an expert.

As with silver; pictures; china etc., there are many pitfalls. All antique clocks are not genuine, and while each individual part of a clock — case, movement, dial — may be old, it is possible they were not made and assembled by the same craftsman originally. Such clocks are known as 'marriages'. These clocks fall in value considerably and they become 'furnishing pieces'.

Many fine antique clocks have been converted from the verge escapement to the anchor escapement — this applies to bracket

v

clocks as there were very few long case or grandfather clocks fitted with verge escapements — and also some of the striking parts may have been removed.

The former practice was more or less legitimate, as it was deemed at the time of conversion that timekeeping would be improved; only in recent years — say since 1900 — have such clocks been appreciated as antiques.

Where parts have been removed, such as pull quarter work, it is inexcusable, and no doubt the result of ignorance.

Even so, clocks so treated can be restored to their original condition, and their value not materially adversely affected.

This kind of restoration is costly, running to £100 and more, but if the clock is by an eminent maker it is worth the expenditure.

With second-hand clocks, such as those of good quality made about 1830–1900, vandalism is not so prevalent, and it is difficult to say why. Maybe the mechanism was more standard and clockmakers understood the working; there was no pull quarter work, or different systems, and of course it could be that clock repairers became more educated as time progressed.

At the Clockmakers Heritage Exhibition held at the Science Museum in London, a certain Tompion bracket clock was exhibited. A visitor recognised the clock, and eventually showed a member of the committee who organised the Exhibition, of which I was a member, the invoice dated, if I remember rightly, 1905, listing two clocks, the first by Joseph Knibb for £6 and the Tompion clock for £4.

The Tompion is, at the present time worth £7,000 — £8,000 and the Knibb clock £3,500 — £4,000.

Tompion left an estate worth £9,000, and since 1700 the pound has appreciated about 20 times, so the estate would be worth £180,000.

A walnut longcase Tompion clock, invoiced by Tompion for £17 10s. plus 20 times is equivalent to £350, but such a clock is now worth from £5,000 — £8,000, and the point I wish to make is that value is not wholly controlled by inflation.

Whether prices will increase at the same rate as they have done over the past 20–30 years is anybody's guess.

Even while this book is being printed and published the values of some of the clocks by important makers, can increase.

I am gratefully indebted to Professor D. S. Torrens, who has kindly read through the transcript and made useful suggestions, and also to Eric Bruton, the Editor of 'Retail Jeweller', for his considerable help. My thanks are also due to J. E. Coleman of the U.S.A.

Before this book was published, Professor Torrens died. He will be missed by many interested in horology as well as by many more in the medical profession.

CONTENTS

A

Acorn Clock   1850

An American shelf clock (q.v.) resembling an acorn. These clocks, now rare, were the product of the Forestville Manufacturing Co. of Forestville, Connecticut, U.S.A.

Acorn clocks are of special interest to Americans. Their value would be in the region of £50.

Act of Parliament Clock   1797

Between 1797–1798 a tax was imposed on all clocks. During this period domestic clocks, in the majority of instances, were put away and not used. A distinct form of clock became popular and was used by inn-keepers as an attraction and the illustration is a typical example. The case was of mahogany, painted or lacquered. No bezel or glass was fitted and usually the clocks were weight-driven timepieces, non-striking.

The imposition of the tax was short lived owing to the difficulty of collecting and also to protests from the clock-making industry.

The style of the case however persisted and was developed well into the 19th century. Some fine examples are to be found both with timepiece and striking movements and fitted with a bezel and glass.

Sometimes referred to as tavern clocks.

The value of these clocks depends upon the quality and decorative merits of their cases but usually ranges from £20 to about £75.

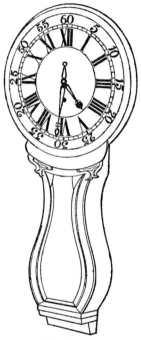

Act of Parliament Clock

See STAGE COACH CLOCK.

Ados Clock

See CAMERA CLOCK.

Alarm clocks date back even before the advent of the clock as a timepiece. Such devices were used to call a person to strike a bell manually, such as a call to prayers in a monastery. At a later date—about 1675—alarm mechanism was incorporated in the BRACKET CLOCK (q.v.). The illustration below is of a typical example of a lantern clock fitted with alarm mechanism. The alarm is driven by a weight and the setting is by the small dial in the centre, set against the tail of the hour hand.

The method of winding some alarms is to draw a cord which winds the alarm mainspring.

The French introduced alarm mechanism into their CARRIAGE CLOCKS (q.v.) about 1865 and the illustration is a typical example.

At the end of the last century Germany produced huge quantities of a simple type of alarm clock which sold in the shops for 1/6–1/11. In more recent years the alarm clock trade has been in the hands of the

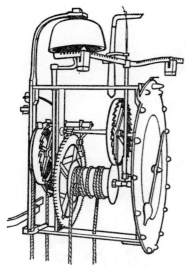

Early Gothic Alarm

Early English Alarm Clock

French Carriage Alarm Clock

English, Swiss, French, and Germans, and the clocks have developed into smart travel and mantle clocks. Some run for 30 hours and others 8 days.

See also PISTOL ALARM CLOCK.

German Alarm Clock

Altar Clock 1660

In the middle of the 17th century clocks were produced in the southern part of Germany in the form of a church altar. They are among the first with cases of wood.

There is no specific market value for this type of clock but a fair estimate would be up to £50.

Anchor Escapement

Alternative name for recoil escapement. Invented about 1656 and attributed to Dr. Robert Hooke. Some authorities attribute the invention to William Clement. The anchor escapement was not in general use until about 1800 but it was used in longcase clocks from its inception because it allowed a small arc of vibration to the pendulum.

The VERGE ESCAPEMENT (q.v.) was universally used with the short pendulum.

Altar Clock

Anniversary Clock

Another name for YEAR CLOCK (q.v.).

Anchor Escapement

3

Appointment Clock 1891

First devised by Davidson and known as a memorandum clock, the system is a clock-operated slot machine.

It consists of a drum with slots marked with hours. The appointments are written on ivory tablets and placed in the slots.

At the appointed hour a tablet is ejected and an alarm bell rings.

A modern version is in the form of a desk pad with hours marked down one side. A built-in clock moves an indicator down the list of appointments.

Arch Top Clock 1790

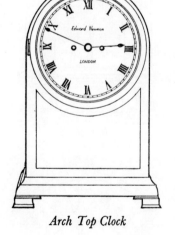

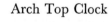
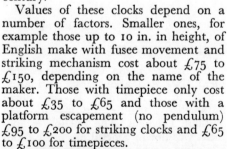

Refers to the top of the case of a clock when it is a complete unbroken arch. First appeared at the end of the 18th century.

Values of these clocks depend on a number of factors. Smaller ones, for example those up to 10 in. in height, of English make with fusee movement and striking mechanism cost about £75 to £150, depending on the name of the maker. Those with timepiece only cost about £35 to £65 and those with a platform escapement (no pendulum) £95 to £200 for striking clocks and £65 to £100 for timepieces.

If the clock is by an eminent maker the value could be increased by 50 per cent.

Large clocks, usually with pendulums, are about half of the values quoted.

Arch Top Clock

Architectural Top Clock 1650

Also known as pediment top. The triangular part at the top of the clock is like that crowning the front of buildings of Grecian, Roman, and Renaissance style. Found in early clocks during the transitional period from the LANTERN CLOCK style (q.v.) of metal case to the cases made of wood, usually ebony veneer or ebonised.

Value of this type of clock when the date is about 1800 and later is similar to that of the ARCH TOP CLOCK (q.v.). The early clocks of circa 1650 by the master clockmakers such as Edward East etc. can be valued at anything from £1,500 to £4,000 and £5,000.

Architectural Top Clock

Arrow Clock   1675

An arrow, secured to a chain, travels round the frame of a mirror. The chain is activated by an 8-day clock mechanism.

There is no record of who invented this type of clock and it may well be that prodigious inventor and maker, Grollier de Servière.

Wood's 'Curiosities of Clocks and Watches', published in 1866, records—'Nicholas Grollier de Servière was born at Lyons 1596 where he died in 1689.

'At the age of 14 years he was a soldier . . . lost an eye at the seige of Verciel. . . . His knowledge of mathematics and mechanics enabled him to render much help to his country during the seiges of the time of Louis XIV. After many adventures he retired from service and found leisure to invent and manufacture many curious clocks and ingenious toys.'

This type of clock is very rare and could be valued at anything from £200 to £300.

Arrow Clock

Artificial Clock

Early name for a mechanical clock, to distinguish it from a natural clock, such as the earth, sun, or moon.

5

Astrolabe Clock 1690

Astrolabe clocks are rare. The dial of a longcase astrolabe clock, made by Thomas Tompion, is illustrated.

The astrolabe was an instrument used by the Greeks and Arabs, and in medieval Europe, to take the altitudes and to mark the positions and movements of heavenly bodies, so as to deduce time and latitude. At the period when astrolabes were first in use, they were not attached to clocks.

The Tompion clock illustrated could be worth between £10,000 and £15,000 and a clock by a lesser maker between £1,000 and £1,500, depending upon the case and the height of the clock. Long case clocks, up to say 6 ft. 6 in., are the most desirable and therefore of greater value.

Astrolabe Clock

Astronomical Clock 1600

A precision clock as used by astronomers. See REGULATOR.

Also refers to a highly complicated clock which not only shows the time of day (mean solar time) on a 12 or 24 hour dial, but also sidereal time (time by successive transits of a star). In addition, the clock might show times at the principal cities of the world; the position of certain planets; day of the week, month, etc.; age of the moon; equation of time, and in some clocks much other astronomical information.

The illustration is of a dial of a typical astronomical clock, and there are other examples where different information is shown.

Makers had their individual ideas, or clients' instructions, regarding the extent of astronomical work required. An astronomical longcase clock made by Edward Cockey for Queen Anne (1705)

Astronomical Dial

has a 24 hour dial, calendar work showing day of month and month of year, rising and setting of the sun, age and phase of the moon, and sidereal time, in addition to the normal mean solar time.

An antique astronomical clock, such as that by Edward Cockey, could be worth £1,500 to £3,000.

Atmos Clock   1930

A clock which is wound by changes of temperature. The principle was first devised by a Frenchman named Reutter. The system then was to use changes of atmospheric pressure, hence the name 'Atmos'.

The present Atmos clock uses a change of temperature to wind the mainspring. An aneroid type of box filled with ethyl chloride responds readily to changes of temperature. The inward and outward movement of one side of the aneroid box winds a small mainspring. It is claimed that a variation of 2°F in temperature is sufficient to keep the clock running for 48 hours.

The mechanism of the clock is in principle similar to that of the 400 DAY CLOCK (q.v.).

The clock is made in Switzerland by Messrs Le Coultre.

Atmos Clock

Ato Clock   1920

A battery-driven electric pendulum clock invented by Hâtot of Paris. It is at present time made by Junghans of Schramberg, West Germany.

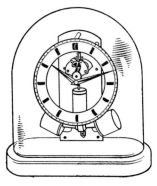

Ato Clock

7

Atomic Clock
See CAESIUM CLOCK.

Automat Clock   1750
Also known as automaton clock. A scene is enacted as well as the clock showing the time of day, striking the hours, and in some cases chiming and perhaps playing a tune.

There are various devices; in one example, each hour or three hours, a mechanism is set in motion and figures painted on metal move before a painted scene. The sails of a windmill revolve, the door of a barn opens and a man appears, raises a gun and shoots a bird which is passing in the air, the bird falls, the gun drops to the man's side, he retreats into the barn and the door closes. The scenes are repeated either at will by pulling a cord or automatically at predetermined times.

The illustration is of a bronze clock with ormolu mounts. The clock movement is at the top and strikes the quarter hours. At the hour or at will, a hornpipe is played on bells in the base of the clock; in the lower tier glass rods rotate to simulate a waterfall; at the centre tier two shutters open and a brilliantly coloured paste flower emerges forwards and rotates then slowly withdraws, devouring a butterfly. At the top of the clock a lotus flower opens and slowly closes.

The clock stands about 2ft 6 inches high.

The first clocks were really automats, they had no dial or hands, see 'Striking Jack'.

The term 'automata' covers a very wide range and includes clocks valued at anything from £350 to £1,500 and more.

Automaton Clock

Automaton Clock
See AUTOMAT CLOCK.

Ball & Tape Clock 1675

A sphere containing a clock mechanism with no mainspring. A tape upon which the hours are marked emerges from the ball and it is the weight of the ball which provides the motive power. As the ball falls, the hour of the day is exposed, the clock being hung from a bracket on a wall.

The clock is wound by lifting the ball so that the tape recedes into it. The duration of run is usually 24 hours.

Value: £100 to £1,500. Reproductions are worth about £50.

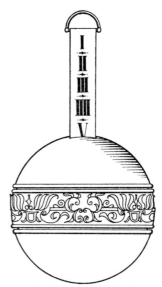

Ball and Tape Clock

Ball Clocks 1675

Several clocks employing a ball, in place of a pendulum or balance were invented by Grollier de Servière. G. H. Baillie in 'Watchmakers and Clockmakers of the World' records, of Grollier, —'Designed and made a number of freak clocks, described in a book published by his grandson, entitled, *Recueil d'ouvrages curieux du cabinet de M. Grollier de Servière. Lyons 1719 and 1733.*'

See ARROW CLOCK and FALLING BALL CLOCK, invented by Grollier. See also FAN CLOCK and CONGREVE CLOCK.

Value: £100 to £1,500.

Balloon Clocks 1750 1750

Refers to the shape of the case of the clock. They are to be found in sizes from 8 inches to 12 inches high and even taller.

The case is usually of satinwood, but examples are seen in mahogany and also ebonised and ebony veneered.

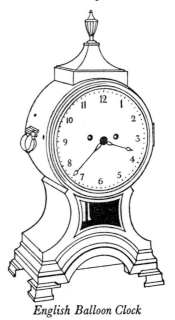

English Balloon Clock

9

The mechanism is generally English. Some important clockmakers as Vulliamy, Dwerrihouse, Holmes, and others have used this style of case.

Occasionally balloon clocks are to be found with French movements, but they are of more recent date, about 1900.

About the middle of the 19th century, ballooning became popular. Articles made of china were decorated with pictures of balloons, pin cushions were made in the form of balloons, and then clocks joined the fashion.

The illustration is of a fine quality French clock in the form of a balloon. The French pillars and clock case are of white marble with ormolu mounts, it stands about 12 inches high.

French Balloon Clock

If the clock is of English make and early 19th century date with fusee movement, the value tends to vary considerably depending on the name of the maker and quality of the movement and case. A small clock, say up to 10 in. high, would be about £100 for a time piece and £250 for a striking clock. Reproductions with a French movement, on the other hand, probably cost just a few pounds.

The original French antique clock, as illustrated, would cost between £250 and £500.

Banjo Clock   1801

An American clock originated by Simon Willard, the eighth child of a family of twelve, born in Grafton, Mass., U.S.A. The name is taken from its banjo-like appearance. The original Willard banjo clocks are much sought after.

These are well made weight-driven pendulum clocks, both timepiece and striking movements. The cases, made to hang on the wall, are well made and beautiful to behold. They have a brilliant appearance, as the panels are of painted glass. The clocks are about 32 inches tall.

A good reproduction of a Willard clock is made by the CHELSEA CLOCK CO. (q.v.) of America.

This type of clock is of particular interest to Americans. A model by Willard could be worth anything from £150 to £300 and one by a lesser maker about £75.

Banjo Clock

Barograph Clock   1900

An instrument which records the change of atmospheric pressure by inking upon a chart which is fixed to a rotating drum. The drum is fitted with an 8-day movement.

A similar system is employed in the instrument that records changes of temperature, the THERMOGRAPH (q.v.).

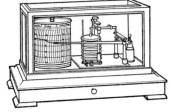

Barograph Clock

Basket Top Clock

Basket Top Clock 1700

Refers to the pierced ormolu top of the clock case. First appeared at about the close of the 17th century. The illustration is a typical example of an English clock.

These clocks have a very wide range of values, one by Tompion being worth from about £5,000 to £8,000 or, by a lesser maker, anything from £350 to £2,000. A clock with a walnut or king-wood case could be worth £1,500 to £2,500.

Battery Clock 1840

An electrically-powered clock employing an electric battery invented by Alexander Bain in 1840. The popular battery clock embodies an electric contact escapement e.g. the BULLE CLOCK (q.v.). Others use the electrical power to wind up at frequent intervals a short mainspring of a conventional clock train. See also SECTICON CLOCK and ATO CLOCK.

'Bee' Clock 1900

A small metal drum alarm clock made in the U.S.A. and fitted with a main-spring the diameter of the clock itself. The winding key is a flat bar with up-turned ends, also the same diameter as the clock.

Belfry Clock

The term 'belfry clock' has been used by some recent writers to refer to a style of table clock.

See TURRET CLOCK, VERTICAL TABLE CLOCK.

Bell Top Clock   1720

Refers to the top of the case of a clock where the form is similar to that of a hand-bell. First appeared during the last quarter of the 17th century.
Value: Very much depends on the maker, size and quality of the case. As an example, a clock by Thos. Tompion could be worth from £7,000 to £10,000 and one by a lesser maker from £650 to say £2,000. A clock by Joseph Knibb would be worth from £4,000 to £6,000.

Bell Top Clock

Big Ben   1859

The great clock at Westminster Palace, the Houses of Parliament. Designed by Lord Grimthorpe and made by Messrs. E. J. Dent. First set going in the Tower at Westminster in May 1859.
The double three gravity escapement was invented by Lord Grimthorpe (Edmund Beckett) especially for Big Ben.
The name really refers to the hour bell. The clock was always called by Grimthorpe 'the Westminster clock'. The hour bell was named after Sir Benjamin Hall, the Chief Commissioner of Works (afterwards Lord Llanover), a big man in stature.
The cost of the clock, including the bells, dials and hands etc., was £22,014.

Data Concerning Big Ben
Height of clock tower, 300 feet.
Height of clock tower to centre of hands, 180 feet.
There are 292 steps to the clock room.
The dials are 22½ feet in diameter or nearly 400 feet in area.
The minute hands are 11 feet long with 3 feet counterpoise.
The hour hands are 9 feet long.
The minute hands weigh 2 cwt. each.

13

'Big Ben'

The four pairs of hands weigh about 1 ton.
The minute spaces are 1 foot square.
The figures are 2 feet long.
The size of the clock room is 28 feet by 18 feet.
The size of the clock mechanism is 16 feet by 5 feet 6 inches.
The pendulum is a shade over 13 feet (to centre of oscillation) and beats 2 seconds.
Weight of pendulum is about 700 pounds.
One ounce, or $\frac{1}{11200}$th part of the weight of the pendulum, on the collar at the middle of the pendulum, will accelerate it 1 second per day.
A penny placed on the tray near its suspension makes the clock gain $\frac{3}{5}$th of a second per day and a halfpenny $\frac{1}{5}$th of a second per day. These coins are actually used by Messrs. Dent today.
The weight that drives the going train is $1\frac{1}{2}$ cwt.
The weight that drives the striking train is $1\frac{1}{2}$ tons.
The weight that drives the chiming train is $1\frac{1}{2}$ tons.
The bell named 'Big Ben' weighs $13\frac{1}{2}$ tons.
The largest of the chime bells weighs 4 tons.
The other chime bells $33\frac{1}{4}$ cwt., 26 cwt., and 21 cwt.
The weight of the hammer which strikes the hour bell is 4 cwt.
When the clock was wound by hand it took 10 minutes to wind the going train and it went for 8 days; the striking and the chiming trains took two men 5 hours and needed winding three times weekly.
The note of the hour bell is E, and the bell is 9 feet in diameter and 9 inches thick. The chime bells' notes are B, E, F, and G, and their diameters are 6 feet, $4\frac{1}{2}$ feet, and 3 feet 9 inches respectively.

The electric motor to wind the clock was installed in 1913 and it now takes 40 minutes to wind all three trains three times weekly.

The first quarter of the chime takes about 2 seconds, the second quarter about 5 seconds approximately, the third quarter takes 8½ seconds. The lapse between the last quarter and the first stroke of the hour is about 10 seconds; and the time between each stroke of the hour is about 4½ seconds. The time elapsing between the beginning of the first phrase and the last stroke of 12 o'clock is about 1 minute 10 seconds.

The first blow on the hour bell denotes the hour.

The lighting of the dials of Big Ben:

From 1859 to 1900, gas lighting was used with Bray burners.

From 1900 to 1905, experiments were carried out with incandescent burners and high pressure gas.

From 1905 to 1906 electric lighting experiments were made with Nernst and mercury vapour lamps.

From 1906 onwards, electric lighting has been used and at present ten 100 watt gas filled lamps are installed for each face.

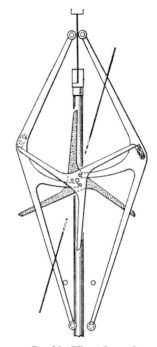

Double Three Legged Gravity Escapement as used in "Big Ben"

During the stonework restoration of the clock tower in 1934, the iron framework of the dials was cleaned and painted and the stonework surrounding was painted and gilded. The weight of gold used was 26 ounces and 32,500 sheets of gold leaf were applied.

The clock faces are washed every three years.

Other than stoppage for overhaul or summer time, Big Ben has stopped in—

1928. Snow became frozen on the east face and held up the minute hand.

1934. A tarpaulin on scaffolding was blown on to the south face and held up the minute hand.

15

1936. A workman leant a ladder against the hand shaft.

1941. The suspension spring of the pendulum broke.

The chimes of Big Ben are taken from Great St Mary's Church, Cambridge (1793-4).

The Westminster Chimes

For the Cambridge clock Dr. Jowett, a member of the University, consulted with a Mr. Crotch and between them they selected a phrase from the fifth bar of Handel's Messiah, 'I know that my Redeemer liveth' and evolved the present chime. Lord Grimthorpe chose this chime and remarked that it was strange that so many young men had listened to the chimes while at the University but no attempt had been made to reproduce them elsewhere. Since then the chime—now known as the 'Westminster chime'—it is the most popular of all used in both public and domestic clocks. The chime is known at Cambridge as 'Jowett's jig'.

The Chimes of "Big Ben"

Billiards Clock

A form of time switch controlled by a clock. Insertion of a coin turns on the lights for a pre-determined period. Another system releases and eventually traps the balls after a given lapse of time.

Bim-Bam Clock

See TING-TANG QUARTER CLOCK.

Birdcage Clock   1775

A singing bird in a cage with a clock movement housed in the base of the cage. Some have the dial and hands on the under side of the cage so that they are visible when the cage is hung up; others have the dial and hands set into the side of the base. At each hour the bird mechanism is set into motion and the bird flutters its wings and turns its head from side to side; then the beak opens and the song starts. The notes are produced by reeds or a whistle and air is blown through by bellows.

Depending upon its importance, an antique birdcage clock could be worth between £1,000 and £2,000. Reproductions, on the other hand, are obtainable for a few pounds.

Black Forest Clock   1680—9

A special type of clock made mainly of wood, fitted with VERGE ESCAPEMENT (q.v.) and FOLIOT (q.v.); one hand, and striking originally on a glass bell. Said first to have been made by Lorenz Frey, a carpenter, of Spurzen, near St Margen, Germany, about 1680. He may have copied a clock made of metal.

There is doubt about who actually made the first Black Forest clocks. Prof. Kistner, who was a leading authority on Black Forest clocks and their history, mentions one Kreuz, of Rodeck, near Furtwangen, Germany, 'about the middle of the 19th century'. He gives 1690 as the date of Lorenz Frey's clock, and refers to the probability of his having copied a clock brought back from Bohemia by an acquaintance.

The fact is that there is no reliable history of the origins of Black Forest clockmaking. There are good records from about 1700 onwards, when the industry became established there.

At the present time the term 'Black Forest' refers to any clock made in this part of Germany, especially CUCKOO CLOCKS (q.v.).

There is no real market value for antique Black Forest clocks and they cannot be worth more than a few pounds.

Bird Cage Clock

Book Clock 1670 and 1930

Metal clock case in the form of a book The cover opens and exposes a clock set into the body of the 'book'. The 'book' opened enables the clock to stand upright. German make.

About 1930 the Swiss produced a leather covered book clock. The cover was spring loaded, and opened it exposed an 8 day CALLOTTE (q.v.) type of clock set into a hinged inner lid—or page—and the cover made to bear upon the edge held the clock up at an angle.

An antique book clock can be valued at the same price as a MONSTRANCE CLOCK (q.v.).

Bookmaker's Bag Clock 1890

A special bag with a time lock used for betting slips collected by the bookmakers' assistants. At a certain time just before the race starts, the bag is closed and this starts the clock.

The slot into which the slips were passed closes and cannot be opened until the bookmaker himself unlocks the bag when he can ascertain the time of the closing of the slot.

The necessity for such a device does not now arise, since the introduction of the Betting Act.

Boudoir Clock 1860

While boudoir suggests a bedroom or a small apartment for a lady, the term 'boudoir clock' has become associated with a particular type of clock such as the one illustrated.

These clocks are of brass, engraved and gilt, and usually with some device such as a strut or swivel foot so that the clock can be made to stand up and to fold flat for travelling. Many are beautifully made with English 8 day movements, some to strike the hours and others

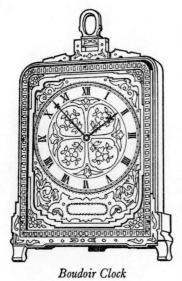

Boudoir Clock

18

with calendar work and engraved silvered dials.

The original English boudoir clocks can be valued at from £100 for a timepiece and £150 for a striking clock, much depending on the quality and importance of the case, etc.

Boulle or Buhl Clock 1642 and 1723

Refers to the case of the clock where a veneer of tortoiseshell is used inlaid with brass, and more rarely inlaid with ivory, silver, etc.

The style was invented or created by André Charles Boulle, the French cabinet maker. Not only clock cases but small articles of furniture and desk appointments were so decorated.

These clocks can have a very wide range of values. Antique Buhl clocks can vary from say £350 to £1,500, depending on the importance of the clock and the maker's name.

Reproductions made during the last century can be valued at from £35 to £85.

Box Chronometer 1760–70

An instrument of precision used on board ship; not necessary as a timekeeper only but to ensure that Greenwich Mean Time is available for purposes of ascertaining, with the aid of a sextant, the longitude and the position of the ship while at sea.

So important was the necessity for G.M.T. at sea that in 1714 the British Government offered an award of £20,000 to any person who would provide a timekeeping device which would remain 'accurate' while at sea. John Harrison, a Lincolnshire carpenter turned clockmaker, eventually gained the prize.

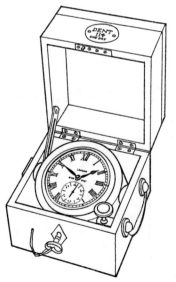

Box Chronometer

The chronometer (bearing no resemblance in any respect to the Harrison instrument) was developed and perfected by John Arnold and Thomas Earnshaw from the original invention of Pierre le Roy about 1748.

The Marine Chronometer of the present time first appeared after the middle of the 18th century and the special feature of this instrument is the CHRONOMETER ESCAPEMENT (q.v.). The mechanism is mounted in gymbals—a universal joint—so as to maintain the instrument in a horizontal position during pitching and rolling of the ship while at sea.

Chronometers were not 'boxed' much before 1770, or even later. Kendall probably made the first 'boxed' chronometer.

The word 'chronometer' means time measurer and was much abused by watch manufacturers on the continent who marked all and sundry watches as chronometers. Later the Swiss decreed that a watch to be entitled to be known as a chronometer must pass certain specified tests in a laboratory.

An English box chronometer with detent escapement can be valued at from say £35 to £200.

Early Bracket Clock

Bracket Clock   1659

Such clocks were so-called because it was assumed that they were made to stand on brackets, but there is no evidence that brackets were used. They were apparently made to stand upon tables, as at this period clocks were scarce and were moved from one room to another.

The first illustration is a typical example of an early bracket clock of architectural form and the second a fully developed bracket clock with break arch dial.

The term 'bracket clock' now refers to this particular style of clock, and to modern reproductions of the earlier style.

Modern mantelpiece clocks are also at times called 'bracket clocks' to distinguish them from grandfather and other style of clocks.

Value: Much depends on the maker, size, quality of the case, etc. One by an eminent maker would be from £4,000 to say £10,000. A 19th century English clock would be from £150 to about £350, or, if with chiming movement, up to £600.

Bracket Clock
(*fully developed*)

Breguet Clock   1795

Although the name Breguet does not refer to one particular form of clock, it is used as a description, because Breguet produced many distinctive clocks during his lifetime, from small desk or travel clocks like the one illustrated, to longcase clocks. All are endowed with the Breguet touch.

Abraham-Louis Breguet (1742–1823) was born near Neuchâtel, Switzerland, but he was not known until he became established in Paris in 1787.

In addition to his numerous inventions, which he appears to have just taken in his stride, so prolific was the production of his fertile brain, he created and maintained a distinctive style which has left its mark on everything he touched, even to the kind of lettering on his stationery and the leather covering and tooling of the cases in which he placed the finished merchandise.

The value of a Breguet clock can vary from £500 to £12,000 or more.

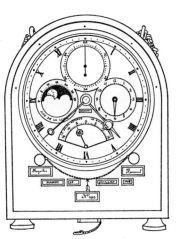

Breguet Clock

Brocot Escapement

Brocot Clock   1850

The name is derived from the name of the inventor and maker, Achille Brocot, Paris (born 1817, died 1878).

Brocot invented the PIN PALLET ESCAPEMENT (q.v.) for pendulum clocks, and a form of pendulum suspension with which it is possible to regulate the clock from the front. The Brocot escapement should not be confused with the pin-pallet escapement used in some low priced watches.

VISIBLE ESCAPEMENT CLOCKS (q.v.) are usually fitted with the Brocot escapement. He also produced PERPETUAL CALENDAR CLOCKS (q.v.).

See FOUR GLASS REGULATOR, which is a Brocot clock.

Brocot Escapement

A form of DEAD BEAT ESCAPEMENT (q.v.) invented by Achille Brocot (1817–1878). This form of escapement was popular with French clockmakers, who were fond of making the escapement visible. See FRENCH FOUR GLASS REGULATOR.

Broken Arch Clock   1780

Refers to a clock case similar to the arch top clock, but the arch is broken by a step on each side.

Value: Up to 10 inches in height, a timepiece would be priced at about £100 and a striking clock at £250. If larger, 25 per cent less. If fitted with a French movement, the value is a few pounds.

Broken Arch Top Clock

Bull Clock 1750

As with the ELEPHANT AND THE LION CLOCKS (q.v.) the name refers to the style of case, a figure of a bull being the feature. They were French made and of good quality.

Many of the animal cases were made by Saint-Germain, the French sculptor.

An antique bull clock with a good quality case by an eminent sculptor and movement by a good maker can be valued at from £750 to £1,500.

A good reproduction made during the latter part of the 19th century can be valued at from £65 to £150.

Bull Clock

Bulle Clock 1910

A battery-driven clock in which the pendulum bob consists of a solenoid which swings to and fro over a permanent magnet. Attached to the pendulum rod near its suspension is a silver pin which makes contact with the plate each time the pendulum swings to the right, thus completing the circuit through the electro-magnet, which causes the pendulum to be repelled from the centre of the permanent magnet, this giving it an impulse to the right. No impulse is given to the pendulum on its return journey.

The current to drive the clock was derived from a 1½ volt battery, which would operate for about 800 days.

The illustration shows the usual style, which is provided with a glass dome. (N.B. not to be confused with *Boulle*, which refers to a type of French furniture decoration.)

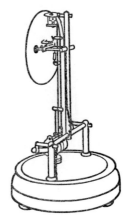

Bulle Clock

C

Caesium Clock

A time standard based on the natural frequency of the caesium atom. The first practical atomic clock was made by Dr. Louis Essen, of the National Physical Laboratory, England, who was helped by pioneer work in the U.S.A.

From June 1955 the QUARTZ CRYSTAL CLOCKS (q.v.) at the N.P.L. were checked by means of an atomic standard. This was the first time quartz clocks had been calibrated with an atomic standard to an accuracy greater than that given by astronomical time.

It was a complete break with the traditional system which is, of course, based on the rotation of the earth.

One complete rotation of the earth gives the day and this is divided into a more convenient and shorter unit by the

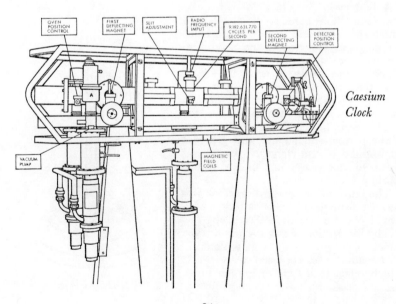

Caesium Clock

steady swinging of the pendulum or, in more recent years, by the rapid vibrations of a ring of quartz.

In practice, because astronomical measurements are relatively inaccurate, the results are averaged over quite long intervals.

The working standards of the time are the quartz crystal clocks, which are adjusted periodically to keep in step, or time, with time as derived from the rotation of the earth. This procedure is no longer accurate enough for some scientific work, because the earth's rotation itself is found to fluctuate during the year, i.e. other than the predictable errors.

To overcome these fluctuations, the observations must be averaged over still longer intervals of several years. The quartz clocks cannot be relied upon to keep uniform time for such long periods. So, although it is possible to know that average value of the unit of time with great accuracy, the value at any particular instant can only be known with a much smaller degree of accuracy. There is the added disadvantage that the results can only be calculated some years in arrears, when sufficient astronomical data has been accumulated.

A standard which is not only more accurate but gives results much more quickly seemed to be that offered by the natural vibrations of the atom. Not all atoms can be used, but the caesium atom is particularly suitable because of its unusual magnetic qualities. It behaves like a tiny compass needle, which can, however, set either along the direction of a magnetic field or in exactly the opposite direction. The state it is in can be recognised by the direction in which it is deflected by a magnet.

It is possible to produce a change from one state to the other by applying a magnetic field which is reversing its direction very rapidly, but only when the frequency corresponds exactly to a particular value which is a fundamental constant of the caesium atom. The reason for this is that a small but very definite amount of work must be done to change the atom from one state to the other.

The frequency required is very high. So far, the most accurate measurements made give it as 9,162, 631, 830 cycles per second.

The first caesium standard was a copper tube 5 ft in length supported on two heavy pedestals, and a system of pipes and pumps to maintain a very high vacuum inside it. Around the tube are a number of coils of wire which are used to apply the appropriate magnetic fields. A smaller copper tube leads away from the middle of the main chamber to a small transmitter, similar to that used in radar equipment, which supplies the rapidly alternating field.

The caesium atoms are evaporated from an oven at one end of the tube; they pass through a fixed magnet, then through the alternating field and then through a second fixed magnet.

When the frequency of the transmitter is just right, the timing magnets spin round, as it were, and they are then passed by the second magnet on the detector so that there is a sharp rise in the number of atoms received.

The transmitter can thus be set at the caesium frequency and then used in turn to calibrate the quartz clocks.

The setting is so exact, even with the first experimental model, that the quartz clocks controlled by the caesium atoms kept time to the equivalent of one second in 300 years.

The caesium standard also has many other scientific uses. One N.P.L. version is employed as well to monitor the standard frequency broadcasts from the Post Office Radio Station M.S.F. at Rugby on 2–5, 5, and 10 mc/s.

The accuracy of the latest atomic clock is in the order of 1 second in 3,000 years. It is not normally kept going continuously but is run when required for frequency comparison purposes.

Calotte Clock

See THREE FOLD CLOCK.

Camera Clock   1930

A travel clock which derives its name from its similarity to a folding camera of the time of its introduction. Messrs Le Coultre of Switzerland have designed a camera clock which they have named Ados.

These clocks are usually of Swiss manufacture.

Ados Camera Clock

Candle Clock   872–900

Reputed to have been used by King Alfred. Notches were cut into the sides of the candle and as it burnt away so the passage of time was noted.

There is no record of the duration of time between each notch, but it could have been as a division of the dark hours since a form of sundial would be used for the light hours. At best it would be crude because the period of darkness varies from season to season. On the other hand the notches could have indicated an arbitrary measure of a period of time.

It is recorded by Asser, King Alfred's biographer, that Alfred used candles which burnt away in four hours, to program his day's work.

Candle Clock

27

French Carriage Clock with Repeating Knob on top

Carriage Clock 1850

The French carriage clock was first seen about 1850. It is probably a development of the French PENDULE D' OFFICIER (q.v.) a kind of desk clock. Soon after its introduction, it became very popular and was made in vast quantities well into the 20th century.

The system of manufacture was similar to that employed by the English watch trade. The movements (mechanism) in the rough unfinished state were made in St. Nicholas, Lyons, and other towns and finished and assembled in Paris by various makers. The platform escapements were made by specialists outside Paris, near the Swiss frontier. The final maker would decide upon the quality of the finish and the quality of the escapement.

Many carriage clocks were produced by makers such as Henri Jacot, M. Drocourt, Paul Garnier, M. Soldano, M. Baveux, and many others, who sold them to retail vendors and placed the vendor's name on the dials.

The cases, gongs etc. were made by specialists and no doubt the vendor would decide what quality of movement, escapement, case etc. he required.

Carriage clocks were made as simple timepieces and alarms and with a variety of complications including:

Striking, sounding one stroke at the half hour and the number of hours at the hour. Some of these have alarms also.

Repeating, where in addition to striking, a push piece at the top of the case causes the clock to strike the previous number of hours.

Quarter strike, also known as 'petite sonnerie', where the clock strikes a ting-tang for each quarter of an hour, one ting-tang at the quarter past the hour, two at the half hour, and three at the quarter to the hour. Also made with repeater push piece.

Grande Sonnerie (q.v.) A full strike where the clock strikes ting-tang at the quarters and the preceding hour at each quarter.

The illustration is of the under side of a grande sonnerie clock showing the lever to operate the full strike, silent and quarters only.

Some carriage clocks are fitted with four gongs to chime at the hours and others have grande sonnerie, in addition.

They were also made as MINUTE REPEATERS (q.v.) where, upon operating the repeater push, the clock strikes the number of hours and quarters, and minutes up to 14 minutes. At the quarter past it will strike the ting-tang and at, say, 20 minutes past the hour a ting-tang and then 5 blows to denote 5 minutes past the quarter hour.

Carriage clocks were also made with calendar work to give the month and the day, and so on almost *ad infinitum*.

The English made carriage clocks in the French style, and some extremely fine examples of craftmanship are to be found, but, as a rule, not with the same amount of complications as the French.

An informative article on French carriage clocks is to be found on page 77 of Vol. IV of *Antiquarian Horology* by A. B. Dickie.

Value: The value of carriage clocks depends upon the quality of movement and complication. The figures give a general guide, the condition of the movement and the case being assumed to be as near new as possible:

Timepiece, with lever escapement from £27 10s. to say £45.

Timepiece with alarm £30 to £47 10s.

Striking clock from say £65 to £95.

Striking clock with repeating work £75 to say £110.

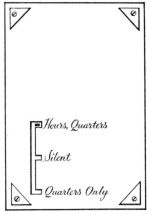

Grande Sonnerie

Quarter striking from £95 to say £110. Grande sonnerie from £150 to say £300 at least.

Where the movement is of exceptionally good quality with a high grade lever escapement, at least 15 per cent can be added to the above prices.

For clocks which have cases with enamel on porcelain panels and dials at least 100 per cent can be added to the above prices, depending upon the quality of the enamel.

For carriage clocks with English fusee and chain movement, the value can be from £300 to £850 if fitted with striking mechanism.

Cartel Clock

Cartel Clock   1750

A clock to hang on the wall; a wall clock of French manufacture usually made of ormolu (bronze) and fire or mercurially gilt. Some beautiful examples are to be found and although the word cartel means 'dial clock', it refers to a particular style of elongated clock.

Some of the cases have been made by eminent French founder-chasers (there is no equivalent in English for *fondeur ciseleur*), artists such as Caffieri, and such case makers as Duhamel.

The value of antique cartel clocks of high quality, especially the case, can be anything from £750 to £1,500.

Less important clocks are valued at from £150 to £350.

Chaise Clock   1750

A clock in the form of a very large watch also called at the present time a GOLIATH CLOCK (q.v.).

Such clocks of the 18th century were in handsome metal cases, sometimes of gold, set with coloured stones and enamelled. They were carried in a pocket inside a chaise or other vehicle.

The illustration is a typical example. Another name is coach clock.

The chaise clock has a wide range of values—anything from say £150 to £1,500. Much depends on the quality and name of the maker.

Chaise Clock

Chamber or Domestic Clock
1400–1500

The first domestic clocks made their appearance about 1470. They were made of iron and had no cases. Drive was by weights.

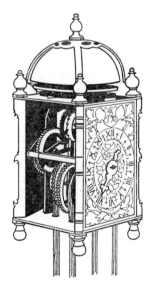

*15th Century
Chamber
Clock* (2)

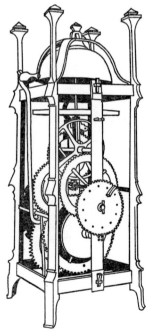

Early Chamber Clock (1)

31

The illustration (1) is of a typical 14th century domestic clock and the illustration (2) is an advanced clock of the late 14th century or early 15th century.

Clocks like that shown in the illustration (1) can be valued at from £200 to £500 and (2) from £150 to £350.

Chamfer Top Clock

Chamfer Top Clock   1810

Refers to a clock case where the top is formed by steps and a bevel or chamfer. Very popular during the Regency period.

Value: Up to 10 inches high, one would be about £100, or £250 if striking. Larger clocks about 25 per cent less.

Chelsea Clock

Chelsea Clock   1886

A high grade clock made in the U.S.A. at Chelsea, a few miles from Boston. The company was first known as The Eastman Clock Co. (1888–1897) and finally as The Chelsea Clock Co. from 1897 to the present day.

Probably the best known clock from this factory is the SHIP'S BELL CLOCK (q.v.) in a copper bronze case. Chelsea has supplied clocks to the U.S. government (Weather Bureau and the Navy) for many years. Each clock is numbered serially and a complete record has been maintained. At one time the platform escapements of Chelsea clocks were made by the Waltham Watch Co. but for many years past they have been made in their own factory.

Chelsea make a complete range of clocks, timepieces and striking fitted into bracket (q.v.) strut (q.v.) and wall clocks, but best known in this country are the ship's bell and the illustrations are typical examples.

Chess Clock   1860

At one time a chess player could take as long as he pleased over a move, thus subjecting his opponent to weariness etc. About a century ago the idea of controlling the time allowance for each player was adopted. At first sand glasses were used; now there are special clocks.

Chelsea Ship's Bell Clock

Two clocks, as illustrated, are used and each clock works independently of the other. Each clock records the time consumed by one of the two players. When a move is made, the player depresses the knob or push button on the top of the clock nearest to him. This automatically raises the knob of the other clock, stopping the player's clock and starting his opponent's. When the opponent has made his move, he reverses the process by depressing the knob his side of the clock.

The time registered on each clock at any moment thus represents the time expended by each player. If a player takes a minute for his first move, two for his second and say nine for his third, then the minute hand will register 12 minutes.

Chess Clock

Each clock has a little red 'flag' suspended near the twelve o'clock mark which is slowly raised to a horizontal position by the minute hand as the latter approaches that mark, and falls again the moment it passes.

A fairly common time allowance for a game is twenty moves for each player per hour. In most games both players make their twenty moves well within the allotted hour but it occasionally happens, when the game has been unusually long or complicated, that one or both have difficulty in doing so.

If a player fails to make his twentieth move before his flag drops for the first time, he automatically forfeits the game, even though he may have an over-whelmingly superior position and may complete his quota of moves an instant later. Each player must likewise have made forty moves before his flag falls again at the end of a further hour of his time, and so on.

Chiming Clock   1700

A clock which chimes at the hours and quarters in addition to striking the hours at the hour. Sometimes a striking clock is referred to, erroneously, as a chiming clock.

First introduced at the end of the 17th century. Up to the last quarter of the 18th century the chimes were on bells. Gongs were introduced about 1870 and tubes and rods a little later.

A chiming clock can usually be distinguished by three winding squares. There are the exceptions where two winding squares are found.

An English chiming clock of the early 18th century can be valued at about £250 to £850, depending on the size, quality, and maker's name. Nineteenth century clocks can be valued at about £75 to £250, much depending on the size, etc.

Chronometer

See Box Chronometer.

Chronometer Clock 1780

A clock fitted with a full CHRONO-
METER ESCAPEMENT (q.v.) i.e. spring
detent, escapement. Often it can be
identified by its helical balance spring.

The word 'chronometer' is now used
to define a watch which has passed
certain tests etc. and can refer to the
lever and even the pin pallet escapement.
Originally it applied to a ship's BOX
CHRONOMETER (q.v.) with a spring
detent escapement.

A true chronometer escapement fitted
to a clock adds considerably to its value.
In the section on CARRIAGE CLOCKS the
value of an English timepiece clock with
fusee and chain movements and lever
escapement is given at about £200 to
£500. With a chronometer escapement
it could be worth £50 to £100 more.

Chronometer Escapement 1748-1780

Originally invented by Le Roy and
improved by other French horologists.
Arnold, the English horologist made
further improvements, introducing the
long spring detent and about the same
period, 1780, Earnshaw perfected the
escapement. The illustration is of the
Arnold escapement.

The advantage of the chronometer
compared with the LEVER ESCAPEMENT
(q.v.) is that it does not require oil,
except to the pivots. Therefore the
timekeeping rate is not affected through
deterioration of oil.

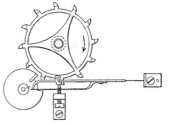

Chronometer Escapement
(Arnold)

Clepsydra Clock 1500 B.C.

See WATER CLOCK.

Column Clock

Coach Clock
See CHAISE CLOCK.

Column Clock   1700
A fairly popular style of clock in France during 18th and 19th centuries. The style originated with a bracket clock standing upon a pedestal, where the pedestal was made of the same material as the clock case. The style developed and the pedestal became an integral part of the case. The clock still retained the short pendulum of the bracket clock.

During the first quarter of the 18th century the long pendulum was introduced, with a glazed door through which it could be seen. Cases became more elaborate and some beautiful examples of what might be called 'French grandfather clocks' are to be seen.

About 1750, a few clocks of similar style were made, with long pendulum and weight drive known as 'pedestal clocks'.

The value of column clocks depends on a number of factors such as the quality of the movement and, particularly the style of the case and the maker's name. It can be anything between £350 and £2,000.

See FRENCH CLOCKS.

Combination Clock   1930
Similar to the THREE FOLD CLOCK (q.v.) with the addition of another mechanism, which can be a calendar operated from the time clock movement. These calendars are not perpetual but register up to 31 days and therefore must be adjusted manually when there are 30, 28, or 29 days in a month.

Combination clocks are also fitted with barometers. Some combination clocks have four and six mechanisms,

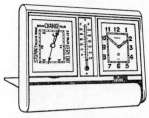

Ados Combination Clock

known as 'foursome' and 'sixsome'. In addition to the time of day they have calendar, barometer, thermometer, hygrometer, and compass.

Comtiose Clock

See MORBIER CLOCK.

Congreve Clock   1808

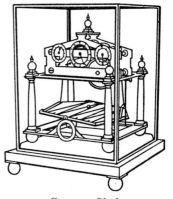

Congreve Clock

A form of ball clock, patented by William Congreve, Comptroller of Woolwich Arsenal, which, at first glance, gives the impression of perpetual motion.

A steel ball—a large ball bearing—rolls along a zig-zag grooved track on a plate which is at an angle; when the ball reaches the bottom it strikes a lever which releases a mechanism to tilt the grooved plate in the opposite direction. The ball then starts its journey down the zig-zag path to strike a similar releasing lever at the other end, and so the cycle continues.

Congreve clocks run for 8 days with each winding and, while they are not good timekeepers, they are fascinating to observe.

These clocks may be valued at between £250 and £750, depending on the quality and the age.

Conical Pendulum Clock   1667

Conical Pendulum Clock

A clock of which the pendulum bob describes a circle. The conventional pendulum describes an arc in the same plane.

C. A. Crommelin in his book 'The Clocks of Christiaan Huygens' says when referring to the inventions of Huygens 'the first clock after the invention of the pendulum clock was a timepiece with a conical pendulum invented probably in 1659 or 1660 and constructed about 1667–1668'.

The time of rotation of a conical pendulum is $T = 2\pi \sqrt{\dfrac{L \cos \alpha}{g}}$

where L length of pendulum
  α angle of elevation
  g acceleration due to gravity

For small angles $T = 2\pi \sqrt{\dfrac{L}{g}}$ or the same as the time taken for a double swing of a plane pendulum of the same length.

As there is no escapement in the accepted sense of the term, there is no stop and start but a continuous motion, and for this reason this pendulum is used by astronomers to control equatorial telescopes.

The illustration shows a domestic conical pendulum clock, made about 1885; it is more in the nature of a novelty rather than a serious timepiece.

Although there is no real market value which can be set on these clocks, they sell in the region of £100. There are some cheap versions of the conical pendulum clock worth only a pound or two.

Cordless Clock

An American term for a BATTERY CLOCK (q.v.).

Cottage Clock   1790

A small clock average height 6 inches and usually 2 inches deep, fitted with a 30 hour verge watch sized movement, similar to those fitted to SEDAN CLOCKS (q.v.).

The case is made of wood, rosewood, or mahogany and decorated with brass work.

A good cottage clock, usually fitted with a modern 8-day Swiss movement can be valued at about £35.

Cottage Clock

38

Cross Beat Clock

An example of a Cross Beat Clock is to be seen in the British Museum (Octavius Morgan bequest). It is a German clock dated 1630.

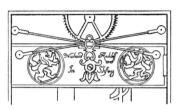

It would appear that the cross beat escapement, from which the clock takes its name, was invented by Jost Burgi of Prague, between 1592 and 1604.

Cross Beat Escapement

The escapement is a form of VERGE (q.v.) with two swinging balance arms which oscillate in opposite directions and therefore keep swinging across each other. Clocks fitted with the cross beat escapement are very rare. Other than the British Museum, examples are to be seen in the Danish National Museum, Copenhagen, and the Treasure Chamber Vienna.

An authoritative article by Dr H. von Bertele on the cross beat and other clocks of the period appears in the *Horological Journal* of December 1953.

There is no real market value: such clocks are of interest to connoisseurs and very rarely come into the market, the value could be very high.

Crown Wheel Escapement

See VERGE ESCAPEMENT.

Crucifix Clock   1625

A gilt metal crucifix with a revolving globe with chapter ring at the top. Stands about 12 inches high. Of German make, usually from Augsburg.

The crucifix clock cannot be given a specific market value but £200 up to £750 would be a good estimate. There are some modern versions which cost only a few pounds.

Crucifix Clock

39

Crystal Ball Clock 1900

A Goliath (large) clock with a half spherical front and back of glass, thus forming a ball. Fitted with 30 hour or 8-day Swiss mechanism.

Made to stand on a desk etc. Some crystal ball clocks are made with a surround of coloured pastes. Of no real value, a few pounds.

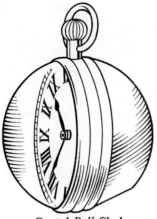

Crystal Ball Clock

Cuckoo Clock 1730

First made by Anton Ketterer of Schonwald, in the Black Forest, Germany, and afterwards made there in large numbers. Often erroneously referred to as of Swiss manufacture.

The feature of the clock is that the hours and half hours are struck on a gong, and a door at the top of the case opens, a wooden model of a cuckoo emerges and a sound similar to the call of the bird is made by two pipes.

See also BLACK FOREST CLOCK.

Cuckoo Clock

Cylinder Escapement 1695

Invented by Tompion, Booth, and Houghton about 1695 and improved by George Graham. Taken up by many makers in France as well as England for watches in the 18th century and during the 19th applied to cheap clocks.

It was superseded by the LEVER ESCAPEMENT (q.v.) although this did not come into general use until almost 100 years after its invention. Another name for the cylinder is the 'horizontal escapement'.

Cylinder Escapement

D

Dashboard Clock   1910

Originally a spring-driven clock fitted on or into the dashboard of a motor car. At the present time dashboard clocks are usually driven from the accumulator of the car.

Davidson's Memorandum Clock

See APPOINTMENT CLOCK.

Dead Beat Escapement

Dead Beat Escapement   1715

An improved form of the ANCHOR ESCAPEMENT (q.v.). Invented by Graham about 1715. Although not as robust as the anchor escapement, it is capable of greater accuracy when used in a clock.

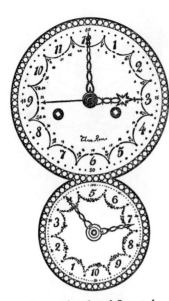

One reason is that it allows of a smaller arc of vibration of the pendulum, which is desirable where precision is required.

The name 'dead beat' is derived from the fact that when a tooth of the escape wheel has dropped on to the pallet the escape wheel does not recoil—as with the anchor escapement—but stays 'dead', i.e. remains motionless, owing to the faces of the pallets being arcs of a circle centred at the pallet arbor.

Conventional and Inverted Decimal Dial

Decimal Dial Clock   1792–1805

During the period of the French Revolution, clocks and watches were made with decimal dials showing 10 hours. Some had both conventional 12 hour and 10 hour dials. The system was decreed by Napoleon I, but was short lived and few specimens are now to be found.

Desk Clock   1956

A development of the STRUT CLOCK (q.v.). As the illustration shows, desk clocks are built at an angle and cannot be knocked over. Usually of Swiss manufacture, with 8-day and battery movements, some are fitted with calendar work, and also can indicate WORLD TIME (q.v.) and have a PERPETUAL CALENDAR (q.v.), alarm, etc.

Desk Clock

Dial Clock   1875

Also known as 'English dial clock', and made for use in an office or kitchen. The timepiece movements of these clocks are usually well made with fusee and chain or line. An inferier version is to be found with a spring-driven German movement.

An English fusee clock dated between 1875 and 1900 can be valued at about £10 for what may be termed an 'ordinary clock'. Some finer quality dial clocks with engraved silvered dials can be valued at about £35. Also antique dial clocks fitted with verge escapement are to be found and can be valued at about £35 to £50.

Dial Clock

Digital Clock

See ELECTRONIC CLOCK.

Directoire Clock   1795

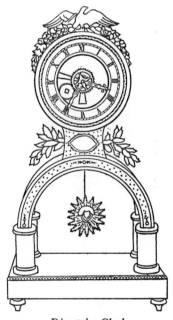

A French style, so called from the French Directory, which was an influence in style from 1795 to 1799.

'Directoire style' is also a loose term designating the transitional style between Louis XVI and the Empire style. It is characterized by a tendency for the purely Roman and Greek motifs.

A good quality clock can be valued at anything from £75 to £500, depending on its importance, style, and the maker's name.

D'Officieur, Pendule Clock

See PENDULE D'OFFICIEUR.

Directoire Clock

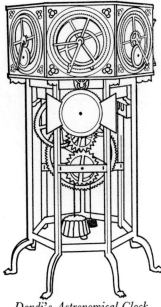

Dondi's Astronomical Clock

Double Basket

Dome Top Clock 1680

Clock with a domed top to the case, which first appeared during the last quarter of the 17th century.

A typical example of an English clock is illustrated under BELL TOP CLOCK.

Value: Similar to that of the ARCH TOP CLOCK (q.v.).

Domestic Clocks 1400–1500

See CHAMBER CLOCK.

Dondi Clock

A complicated astronomical clock showing solar and sidereal time, rising and setting of the sun, and much astronomical information originally made by Giovanni de' Dondi, an Italian professor of astronomy and medicine.

The illustration is of a reproduction of the original clock made in 1963 by Messrs Thwaites and Reed of London under the supervision of H. Alan Lloyd. It is now in the Smithsonian museum in the U.S.A.

Double Basket Top Clock 1750

Similar to the BASKET TOP CLOCK (q.v.) but with a smaller basket on top. First appeared about the middle of the 18th century. The illustration is a typical example of an English clock.

Value: Similar to that of the BASKET TOP CLOCK (q.v.).

Double Dial Clock 1920

There are many styles of double dial clocks; also clocks with three and four dials, e.g. TURRET CLOCKS (q.v.) and outside clocks to be seen hanging over business premises.

About 1920 a double dial clock was introduced for use on a desk etc. So that the time can readily be seen from both sides.

Double Three Legged Gravity Escapement 1856

Invented by Lord Grimthorpe for the Westminster clock, BIG BEN (q.v.) about 1856. The great advantage of this escapement is that it allows a heavy weight to drive the clock without affecting the arc of vibration of the pendulum; therefore the hands of the clock, which are exposed to wind and snow, are not so prone to interference.

The power of the clock mechanism lifts the arms of the escapement which drop under the influence of gravity on the pendulum rod, always applying the same force and so keeping the pendulum vibrating to the same amplitude.

See BIG BEN.

Dresden Clock 1830

Clock with a case made of Dresden china. A feature of these clocks is the china flowers. Often a Dresden clock is of ormolu with china flowers. The mechanism is usually of French make.

The value of a Dresden clock varies tremendously, from a few pounds to between £400 and £500, depending on the quality, particularly of the case.

Dresden Clock

Dressing Case Clock 1875

A French or Swiss timepiece clock about 3 inches high and about 2 inches deep, with a case made of silver, which is polished, engraved, or heavily embossed.

45

Also made of tortoiseshell and tortoiseshell inlaid with silver.

They were designed to fit into a pocket of a travelling dressing case.

A small silver timepiece model can be valued at between £25 and £50 and one with a tortoiseshell case slightly lower.

Drop Dial   1875

Similar to DIAL CLOCK (q.v.) but with an extended lower part of the case to accommodate a longer pendulum. These clocks are of English, American, and German make. The American drop dial clock is sometimes fitted with striking mechanism.

Value: Similar to that of the DIAL CLOCK (q.v.).

Drop Dial Clock

Drum Clock   1875

The term 'drum' refers to the brass case or box into which the clock movement fits. It is drum shaped and it is usual for it to be set into an outer case of wood, etc.

'French drum clock' is a much used term of this type of clock since the movement is usually of French manufacture.

An interesting and well made movement is to be found stamped with the initials V.A.P., Valonge à Paris. Fitted with a TIC-TAC escapement (q.v.) and bob pendulum or a built in lever escapement as distinct from a platform escapement.

Drumhead Clock

Drumhead Clock   1865

Refers to the style of case. Usually this style of clock is fitted with a timepiece movement and rarely with a striking movement. Used in libraries, banks, and offices, it is not truly a domestic clock.

As a rule a drumhead clock is fitted with a pendulum and fusee movement of English manufacture.

The value depends on its quality and the maker's name but could be anything from £35 up to about £100 if it is fitted with an English fusee movement.

Duplex Escapement   1750

Invented by Pierre Le Roy about 1750, the duplex escapement was often used in watches, but rarely in clocks. It is a more accurate timekeeper than the CYLINDER ESCAPEMENT (q.v.) but not as accurate as the LEVER ESCAPEMENT (q.v.) which superseded it.

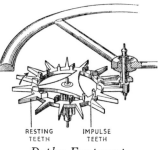

RESTING TEETH   IMPULSE TEETH

Duplex Escapement

Dutch Clocks   1700

Not only is the name derived from the country of origin, but from its distinctive style. Made principally in Friesland and Zaandam (q.v.) and sometimes referred to by these names.

Black Forest clocks are frequently and mistakenly called 'Dutch Clocks' owing to confusion in the past with 'Deutsch'.

In evaluating these clocks much depends on their age and style. The average can be assessed at from £35 to about £200.

Dutch Striking   1690

A system of striking found in some 17th century English clocks and also early Dutch and continental clocks.

The hammer which strikes the bell is fitted to a vertical stem which when operated imparts a horizontal movement to the hammer. The conventional striking is operated by the hammer stem fitted to a horizontal arbor so that the hammer moves in a vertical plane.

E

Egyptian Water Clock   1400 B.C.

A system used by the Greeks and Romans to indicate 'temporal hours'. The vessel is made of stone with an orifice at the base to allow the flow of water.

The inside of the vessel is marked to indicate the hours as the level of the water is lowered. The shape of the vessel is of some importance so as to maintain a constant rate of flow.

For obvious reasons such clocks were poor timekeepers, needing constant checking by means of a sundial. See WATER CLOCK.

Egyptian Water Clock

Electric Clocks   1850

A term referring to clocks which are either driven or controlled by electricity. Clocks with mainsprings or weights wound by electricity, are not truly electric clocks.

Clocks which are wholly dependent upon electric force either from the mains or battery are more accurately called 'electric clocks'.

See MAINS CLOCKS, BATTERY CLOCKS, TRANSISTORISED CLOCKS, BULLE CLOCKS.

Electronic Clock   1952

A clock which is wholly electronic so that there are no wheels, springs, or any moving parts. The clock is actuated electronically e.g. by means of thermionic valves or transistors.

48

The time of day is indicated by light bulbs or tubes. The clock illustrated was developed and made by Patek Philippe of Geneva, Switzerland. The hours, minutes, seconds, and tenths of seconds are indicated graphically by digits similar to the TICKET CLOCK (q.v.). In other words, this version is a digital clock.

Another system is a circle of 60 small bulbs around the perimeter of the dial. One after another is lighted up to indicate the seconds, giving the appearance of the light travelling round the dial. The minutes are indicated in a similar manner as are the hours. There are no hands.

An electronic clock can be operated as a master clock controlling a number of SLAVE CLOCKS (q.v.), with hour and minute hands in the conventional manner, in other places.

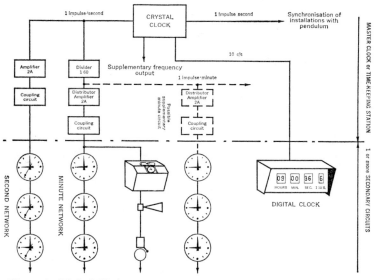

Electronic Digital Clock

Elephant Clock

Empire Clock

Elephant Clock   1765

A style of clock, usually French, employing a model of an elephant as a feature of decoration.

The illustration is a typical example. The value is from £750 to £1,500 for a good clock. Reproductions can be from £65 to say £150.

Empire Clocks   1799–1814

Of French manufacture, and in a typical example, the clock in the first illustration is supported between columns or pillars. The style in the second illustration is of an early Empire clock.

The Empire period also embodies the Revolution clock where the dial records the decimal system of ten hours instead of twelve. This system was shortlived.

The value of an Empire clock depends on the quality of the movement and case. The clock shown in the illustration would be valued at about £750. Clocks of this period can go up to £2,000 or £3,000 depending on the quality of the case and the maker's name.

Engine Clock   1850

The American version of this type of clock has the form of a railway engine. The hours are sounded on the bell of the engine. The steam engine of some American trains is furnished with a large bell, which is rung to announce its approach and to warn cattle off the track.

Another engine clock is in the form of a stationary steam engine, or upright engine, or a beam engine and is of French make.

At the hour, the flywheel, governor and piston rods come to life. In addition to the time of day clock, there are a barometer and a thermometer.

Engine clocks are of interest to Americans and for this reason can be valued at about £50 to £75.

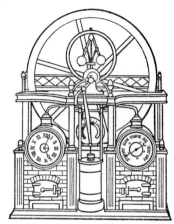

Engine Clock

English Dial

See DIAL CLOCK.

English Four Glass Clock   1850

A clock standing about 6 to 10 inches high and sometimes more. The case is made of wood—mahogany, walnut, rosewood or satinwood—fitted with a fusee pendulum movement, sometimes with a platform escapement. There are timepiece and striking versions. The name comes from the glass panels at the sides, back and top.

Value varies, the smaller clocks fitted with lever escapement £75 for a timepiece and say £100 or more for a striking clock. The larger clocks can be valued at about 25% less. Pendulum clocks at from about £65 for a timepiece to say £100 for a striking clock. A satinwood clock can be valued at about 25% above the prices quoted.

English Four Glass Clock

English Regulator Clock   1750

A weight-driven longcase timepiece clock with a dead beat escapement and compensation pendulum. Sometimes referred to as 'astronomical regulator' or 'Graham regulator', because the dead beat escapement and mercurical pendulum were invented by George Graham.

The dial is divided as shown in the illustration, with a long minute hand, separate hour dial with suitable hand, and seconds dial and hand. Regulators of considerable accuracy were used in observations some years ago, but have been superseded first the FREE PENDULUM CLOCK (q.v.) and then by the QUARTZ CRYSTAL CLOCK (q.v.).

Some English regulators are made to hang on the wall, but are usually made to stand on the floor. They were also sometimes made with GRAVITY ESCAPEments (q.v.).

A regulator made during the 19th and 20th century can be valued at between £75 and £500, depending upon the name of the maker and the clock's height.

Equation Clock   1690

A clock made to show the equation of time automatically on a separate dial. The equation of time is the difference between time shown on the sundial and time in equal hours shown by a clock.

Equation tables were sometimes pasted on the inside door of longcase grandfather clocks.

With the use of the table on the equation dial and a sundial, it is possible to check the timekeeping of the clock.

The value of an equation clock varies considerably. It can be anything from about £200 to £2,500, depending on its age, size, and the maker's name.

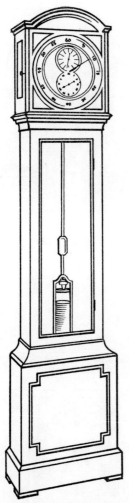

English Regulator Clock

Eureka Clock 1906

An electric battery driven clock, invented by the Kutnow Bros. of America. The system employs a very large balance in place of a pendulum.

A feature of these clocks is the visibility of the balance with its slow backward and forward motion.

Although not antique these clocks are more or less rare and a fair valuation for one in good condition would be between £25 and £50.

Eureka Clock

F

Falling Ball Clock 1685

A form of gravity clock similar to the BALL AND TAPE CLOCK (q.v.). The case is a sphere with a rotating band on which are engraved the hours. A figure, such as a cherub, fixed to the case, indicates the time. A cord wound round a barrel in the sphere allows the clock to descend by reason of its weight. To wind the clock, the sphere is raised.

Original clocks of this description are rare and are therefore difficult to price. A good decorative clock could cost anything from about £100 to £1,500, while reproductions are worth about £50.

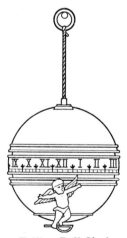

Falling Ball Clock

c

Fan Clock   1650

The fan is made to unfold, exposing the hours, and the time of day is indicated on the left hand side. That in the illustration reads almost 1 o'clock. When the fan is fully unfolded, it snaps back to 6 o'clock and starts to unfold again.

Invented by Nicolas Grollier, afterwards known as M. Grollier de Servière, a remarkable mechanical genius. Born 1593 at Lyons, France he was in early life in the service of the French army. Upon his retirement he devoted his time to designing many kinds of mechanism under the patronage of Louis XIV. He died at the age of 93.

An original fan clock is very rare indeed and would be worth about £350 to £500. A good reproduction could be valued at from £150 to about £250.

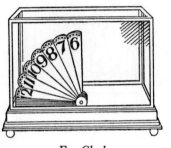

Fan Clock

Fire Clock   1750

A device of Chinese origin, where weights suspended by a thread are burnt at a predetermined time, by means of a fuse, and the weight falls into a metal pan making a clatter.

Flick Clock
See Ticket Clock

Floating Balance Clock   1960

A clock emptying a special type of balance—or rather means of using a balance—in place of a pendulum. Invented by Blesch and Hettich of Germany, and made under licence by Smith's Clocks and Watches.

The purpose of the floating balance is to eliminate some of the difficulty of setting up a clock, particularly those in which a short pendulum is fitted. The balance of the floating balance clock is suspended in such a manner that the clock can be moved without adversely affecting the timekeeping. Also the clock need not stand exactly level as is necessary with a pendulum clock. From the manufacturer's point of view it is less costly to make than the platform lever escapement.

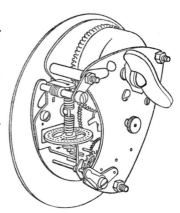

Floating Balance Clock

Floral Clock   1900

A large public clock employing living plants to indicate the dial markings. A good example is to be seen in the gardens in Geneva, Switzerland. The clock is laid out at a slight angle, the hands, some 6 feet long, are gilt metal. The arabic figures of the dial are troughs of flowers or short shrubs and the rest of the dial is planted out with red, green and other coloured plants. The clock has a seconds hand and beats seconds. The mechanism is electric.

Floral Clock

There are many other floral clocks, including those in the Castle Grounds, Edinburgh, the park in Willesden, West London, the garden of the Bulova Watch Factory, Bienne, and Neuchâtel, Switzerland. Some have troughs in the hands to hold plants.

Flying Pendulum Clock

See VILLARD'S ROPE CLOCK.

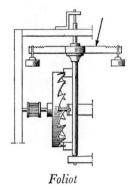

Foliot

Foliot

The original controller of clock and watch mechanism before the balance wheel, and before the pendulum was investigated by Galileo, the Italian scientist about 1640. It was used in conjunction with a VERGE ESCAPEMENT (q.v.) and a crown wheel, as shown in side elevation in the illustration. Under the power of a driving weight, these kept the foliot swinging slowly from side to side, which thus controlled the rate of going of the clock. The weights at the end of the foliot were used to adjust the rate.

Fountain Clock

Fountain Clock   1845

A French clock made to imitate a fountain. A spiral of glass rotates and gives the impression of running water. Clocks are to be seen with three or more spirals appearing to empty water into a receptical containing real water in which goldfish are kept.

The fountain part of the clock is separate from the timekeeping part and is not, as a rule, connected with it. When fully wound, the spirals run for about four hours.

One type of clock has a barrel of red wine as the feature and a thin red spiral of glass rotates to give the impression of wine running into a flagon.

The value of these clocks varies widely since so much depends on an individual model's importance. A fair estimate would be from about £75 for a simple clock up to £200 or even more for an important one.

Four-Hundred Day Clock   1880

Also referred to as 'torsion clock' and 'anniversary clock'. Invented by Anton Harder about 1880 in Germany. Will run for one year with one winding.

These clocks are still made in large quantities in Germany. They employ an ANCHOR ESCAPEMENT (q.v.) with a torsion pendulum. A strip of wire of rectangular form is the pendulum 'rod' and a circular disc or ornamental arrangement constitutes the pendulum bob. The wire pendulum spring is secured at the top. Fixed to this spring is a clip, through which the pendulum receives impulse which twists the wire pendulum 'rod' slowly first one way and then the other.

The principle of the 400 day clock is employed in the ATMOS CLOCK (q.v.).

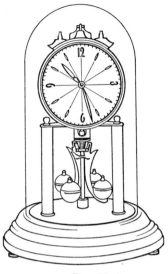

400 *Day Clock*

Free Pendulum Clock   1910

Invented by W. H. Shortt, M. Inst. C.E., the free pendulum clock consists of a pendulum that does nothing but keep time. Another pendulum, the slave, is linked to it electrically to supply impulses when required and to do the work of controlling dials.

The clock on the left of the illustration is the Free Pendulum and the one on the right the Slave Clock.

Up to recent years the free pendulum clock was employed in the most important observations, but has now been superseded by the QUARTZ CRYSTAL CLOCK (q.v.) and the CAESIUM CLOCK (q.v.).

See SHORTT FREE PENDULUM CLOCK.

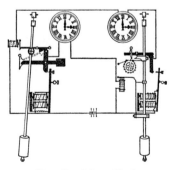

Free Pendulum Clock

French Carriage Clock

See CARRIAGE CLOCK.

French Clocks   1600-1700

During the period 1600–1700 the French developed a style of bracket clock, of which the illustration is a typical example, *circa* 1662 (Louis XVI).

About 1650 (Louis XIV), a distinctive style of clock first as shown in the second illustration. This waisted type of clock persisted well into the 18th century, and vast numbers were made during the 19th century.

About 1780 (Louis XVI), another style appeared having a white marble base with ormolu figures. During this period some of the most beautiful clocks were produced. The cases were designed and made by some of the most distinguished French artists and craftsmen.

At the present time, the Swiss are producing a clock of this form which they call NEUCHATELOISE (q.v.).

Since 1650, French waisted clocks have invariably been made with brackets to match the cases, and the Swiss have followed suit.

André Charles Boulle (1642–1732), a cabinet maker of great repute in Paris, created a style of inlay or marquetery which became most popular, not only for furniture, writing table equipment etc. but also for clock cases. The foundation of Boulle, or Buhl, is tortoiseshell inlaid with brass and sometimes silver and ivory. It is said that Boulle was not the inventor but a master craftsman, improving on the work of renaissance artists in this type of inlay. He was, however, the man who made it popular.

The French also developed a REGU-LATOR CLOCK (q.v.).

See EMPIRE CLOCK.

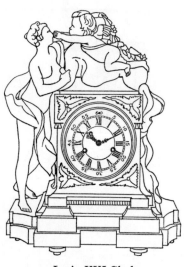

Louis XVI Clock

58

French Four Glass Regulator   1850

A large edition of the FRENCH CAR-RIAGE CLOCK (q.v.) but fitted with a pendulum movement.

The pendulum is usually the Harrison gridiron or the Graham mercurial compensation pendulum. When the gridiron is used, it is often not functional, but used for ornamentation.

The quality of these clocks is generally good. Some have more or less elaborate cases. A plain clock could cost about £25 and a decorative one up to about £100 provided, as for carriage clocks, the condition is as nearly new as possible.

French Four Glass Clock

French Regulator Clock   1750

A precision longcase clock, weight driven, and usually with pin wheel escapement and compensation pendulum. The cases of these clocks are much more decorative than those of the ENGLISH REGULATOR (q.v.) and more suitable for domestic purposes.

The value of French regulator clocks varies considerably according to importance, age, name of maker etc. but a fair estimate would be from about £150 to £1,500.

SEE FRENCH CLOCK for comments on style.

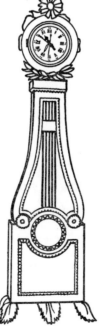

French Regulator Clock

59

Friesland Clock 1700

A particular style of clock, made in Friesland, Holland, to hang on the wall. A feature of these clocks is their highly ornamented cases. Sometimes the weights and the pendulum are enclosed behind the lower part of the case and a glass panel allows the bob of the pendulum to be seen.

The illustration is a typical example.

Also known as ZAANDAM (q.v.) clocks and Stoeltjesklok (little stool clock), although these are earlier than Friesland clocks. Friesland clocks are referred to—correctly—as Staartkloks.

Friesland clocks vary widely in value from about £35 to £200. See DUTCH CLOCK.

Friesland Clock

G

Gensign Clock 1960

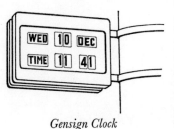

Gensign Clock

An electric clock incorporating the old system of registering the time of day graphically and also the date.

The TICKET CLOCK (q.v.) depicted the time in basically the same manner and the date system has been in use for many years, but this was the first public type of clock to employ both systems at the same time. Made in Italy it is marketed in this country by GENT & Co., Leicester.

Goliath Clock   1880

A large sized pocket watch, usually 8-day, of Swiss manufacture. Also a travel clock, often fitted into an outer case of leather, silver fronted, tortoiseshell, etc., carried in a pocket of a fitted travelling case.

Goliath Clock

Gothic Clock   1450

In architecture, the term refers to the pointed-arch style. With clocks the term refers to a particular style of clock made on the continent from about 1450–1600.

Such clocks were made of iron either to hang on the wall or stand upon a bracket, to allow for the fall of the weights which drive them.

The first illustration is a typical example of an early Gothic clock. The second, on page 62, is of a clock which derives its name from the pointed-arch style.

This cathedral or church style was popular in England about the middle of the 18th century. The cases were usually made of oak.

An original 15th to 17th century Gothic clock could be valued at from £200 to £500.

Early Gothic Clock

Modern 19th century clocks of wood may be valued at up to 25 per cent less than the values as those mentioned for the ARCH TOP CLOCK.

Graham Pendulum

Alternative name Mercurial Pendulum. Invented by George Graham 1721.

The pendulum bob consists of a glass jar (sometimes a metal jar) holding a quantity of mercury. In heat, as the steel pendulum rod elongates so the mercury expands upwards, thus the centre of oscillation of the pendulum remains practically constant.

The Graham pendulum was popular with English makers of precision clocks, such as REGULATORS (q.v.).

Graham Regulator

See ENGLISH REGULATOR CLOCK.

Grande Sonnerie (Full Strike) 1700

The clock strikes both the quarters and the hour at each quarter of the hour.

English late 17th century and early 18th century grande sonnerie clocks chime the quarters and strike the hours at each quarter of an hour.

French carriage Grande Sonnerie clocks—1850—sound the quarters on two gongs—TING-TANG (q.v.) and then the hours.

French carriage Grande Sonnerie clocks can be distinguished by the lever on the under side of the case. There are usually three positions, grande sonnerie, PETITE SONNERIE (q.v.), and silent.

English 17th and 18th century grande sonnerie clocks can be valued at from about £12,000 to £17,000 for a Tompion clock. Clocks by lesser makers cost from

Late Gothic Clock

about £1,500 to £2,500 or even more. (See CARRIAGE CLOCK).

Grandfather Clock
See LONGCASE CLOCK.

Grandmother Clock
See LONGCASE CLOCK.

Gravity Clock   1900
A clock with no mainspring. The weight of the complete clock unit drives the mechanism as it drops slowly down a toothed rack to the base. To wind the clock, the whole unit is lifted to the top of the racked column which passes through or each side of it. Also called a 'rack clock'.

Gravity clocks were made as far back as the 17th century. They are usually of German manufacture. They should not be confused with the GRAVITY ESCAPEMENT CLOCK (q.v.).

These clocks are more or less novelties and are worth only a pound or two, except for the very early ones.

FALLING BALL AND TAPE CLOCKS (q.v.) are really gravity clocks but the term gravity clock refers to the clocks described above.

Gravity Escapement Clock   1860
A REGULATOR CLOCK (q.v.) fitted with a GRAVITY ESCAPEMENT (q.v.) as distinct from the DEAD BEAT ESCAPEMENT (q.v.) which is usual in English regulators.

Gridiron Pendulum
A form of compensation pendulum invented by John Harrison (a Lincolnshire carpenter) about 1725.

The purpose of a compensation pendulum is to correct the error due to

Gravity Clock

63

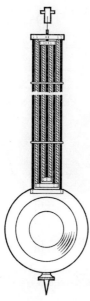

Gridiron Pendulum

changes in temperature. The pendulum rod consists of alternate rods of steel and brass so coupled together that the coefficient of expansion of brass being greater than that of steel compensates for the lengthening of the steel, so that the centre of oscillation of the pendulum remains practically constant during changes in temperature.

The gridiron pendulum was much favoured on the Continent.

H

Hooded Clock
  See WALL CLOCK.

I

Impulse Dial Clock   1900
  See MASTER CLOCK.

Incense Clock   600
  A form of CANDLE CLOCK (q.v.). In place of a candle, a notched incense stick was used.

  The system developed into a flat container with a pattern hollowed out into which the incense was pressed. Lighted at the centre, the incense would burn to the outer edge, passing markings to indicate the hours.

Inclined Plane Clock   1690
  Designed by Nicholas Grollier de Servière about 1690, but also said to

*Inclined
Plane
Clock*

64

have been invented by the Marquess of Worcester and made by Grollier.

A form of DRUM CLOCK (q.v.) fitted with a clock mechanism driven by a weight; the weight is eccentrically placed that in tending to reach its lowest point it drives the clock.

The drum clock runs very slowly down the inclined plane and when it reaches the bottom, it is lifted bodily and re-placed at the top. Originally such clocks ran for 30 hours, but modern versions are made to run for 8 days and in addition, as the illustration shows, can serve as a day calendar.

Original inclined plane clocks are very rare and could be valued at about £200, while a good modern eight-day version would cost around £250. There was also a modern Swiss model available at about £5 to £10.

See FAN CLOCK for notes on Grollier.

Inverted Bell Top Clock 1725

Refers to the shape of the top or dome of the clock case. First appeared about the first quarter of the 18th century. The illustration is a typical example of an English clock.

Value: If up to about 10 inches high, the clock would be about £100 for a timepiece and about £250 for a striking clock. Larger clocks are generally about 25 per cent less, but if fitted with chiming movement, calendar, etc., they would be from £350 to £600.

Inverted Bell Top Clock

J

Japanese Clocks   1650–1866

The Japanese, pre 1873, developed a clock industry peculiar to themselves. The types of clocks they made are unlike any others, both regarding the cases and the methods of recording the time.

After 1873, European timekeeping and calendar were introduced, with the result that the existing clocks became obsolete, European types of clocks superseding them.

J. Drummond Robertson included an exhaustive study on Japanese clocks in his book, 'The Evolution of Clockwork'.

The original Japanese clocks were of six hour duration and the illustration is a typical example of a lantern clock dated 1695. There are no hands. The hour zone rotates and the pointer indicates the hour.

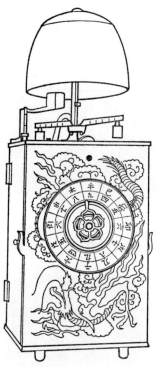

Japanese Lantern Clock

The other illustration is of a pillar clock of about 1830 and the time is indicated by a slide with pointer indicating the hour on the trunk of the clock case. As lengths of hours varied, the hour marks on the case could be altered.

There is no real market value for this type of clock, but they are collector's pieces, worth about £20 to £75 for a timepiece and £200 to £300 for a striking clock.

Japan has now developed a modern horological industry.

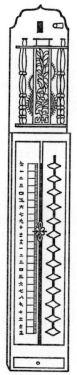

Japanese Pillar Clock

66

L

Lamp Clock   1600

Made about 1600 and originating on
the Continent. It is recorded that this
type of clock was in use up to the end
of the 19th century in outlying country
houses in Germany and Holland. As the
oil burns away, the time is indicated. To
'wind', the vessel is filled with oil. An
excellent night light and clock combined.

Another lamp clock, *circa* 1720, is also
shown. This was made in Germany and
consists of a pewter stand and lamp with
a glass reservoir graduated so that as the
oil burns away the time of day is indicated by the unburnt oil left in the
reservoir.

A cheaper form, made of tin-plate,
was produced in large quantities in the
early part of the 20th century as a form
of advertisement.

These clocks are worth anything from
say, £7 10s. to £10. Antique German
lamp clocks are worth about £35.

Early Lamp Clock

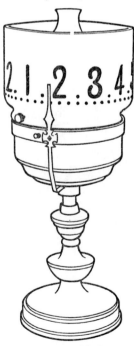

Lamp Clock

Lancet Top Clock

Lantern Clock

Lancet Top Clock 1800

Refers to the top of the case of a clock where the arch terminates in a point. The illustration is a typical example.

Value: About £100 for a timepiece and £250 for a striking clock not more than about 10 inches high, and about 25 per cent less for larger clocks.

Lantern Clock 1620–1700

Also known as 'birdcage', this type of clock seems to have appeared suddenly about 1620. It is a development of the German Gothic wall clock, which had no form of casing at all, the mechanism being quite unprotected as shown in the illustration on page 61.

The illustration below is of a typical English lantern clock, which strikes the hours. Some were fitted with an alarm mechanism. Such clocks were in common use up to the first half of the 18th century.

The early clocks were fitted with a balance; the pendulum did not arrive until about 1657.

Small versions of the lantern clocks were used as travelling clocks. It was not unusual to find a hook in the wall of a bedroom of an inn placed there for visitors to hang their clocks.

Lantern clocks with pendulums first made their appearance about 1700. At lantern clocks were made during Cromwell's time they have come to be known as 'Cromwellian clocks'. All original lantern clocks were made to hang on the wall and were driven by weights and duration of run 30 hours.

Lantern clocks are still produced at the present time, but with spring-driven mechanism, to stand on a table.

Since the original lantern clocks were 30-hour models, they do not command high prices, the average value being about £50 to £100.

If the maker is an eminent one—e.g. Tompion, Knibb, etc.—the clock may increase in value from about £150 to £500.

Lantern clocks fitted with 19th century fusee and chain English movements can be assessed at £65 to £100, this figure being for a striking model.

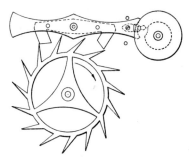

Ratchet Tooth Lever Escapement

Lever Escapement   1770

Invented by Thomas Mudge in 1770 and improved by Josiah Emery about 1780, who made this escapement practicable. The lever escapement is in universal use at the present time.

What is called the 'English lever escapement' has ratchet shaped teeth to the escape wheel as illustrated. The lever escapement in general use has club shaped teeth, as also illustrated, which have the advantage of retaining oil at the active surfaces.

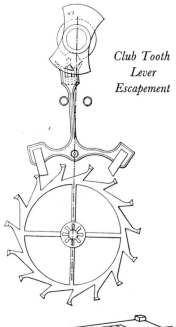

Club Tooth Lever Escapement

Light Clock   1960

A clock where the mainspring is wound by the power of light. Invented by PATEK PHILIPPE of Geneva, Switzerland. The photo cell system is employed to energize a motor which in turn winds the mainspring of a conventional clock, fitted with a lever escapement.

The mainspring when fully wound keeps the clock running for 3 days and if the photo cell of the clock is exposed to light (natural or artificial) for 4 hours the clock will go for 24 hours; therefore if exposed for 12 hours it will run for 3 days in complete darkness.

The clock illustrated is fitted with perpetual calendar mechanism. Other models are made which record the time of day only.

See NIGHT CLOCK.

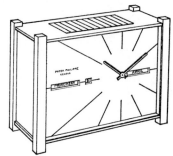

Light Clock

Lighthouse Clock 1850

A table clock in the form of a lighthouse. The clock is fitted in the tower under the 'lamphouse'. A cylinder of glass prisms rotates in what would be the lamphouse.

Such novelty clocks are worth from say £10 to £25.

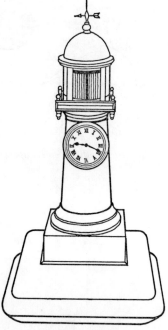

Lighthouse Clock

Lion Clock 1765

A style of clock, usually French, employing a model of a lion as a feature of decoration. The illustration is a typical example.

The base made of white marble decorated with ormolu mounts. The figure of a lion is in bronze and the clock is of ormolu.

The value is from £750 to £1,500 for a good quality clock. Reproductions are about £65 to £1,500.

Lion Clock

Longcase or Grandfather Clock 1660

The first illustration is of the earliest known longcase clock, made by Ahasuerus Fromanteel, the famous Dutch clockmaker, *circa* 1660. The style of the hood is known as architectural, and it will be noted that it is similar to the clock by Edward East illustrated under WALL CLOCK (q.v.).

During this period (1660) the minute hand appeared. With the introduction of the pendulum (after 1657) timekeeping became more accurate, so the minutes were of some importance. The seconds hand appeared about 1675.

The longcase clock was developed and the second illustration is a typical example. This one has the form of dial known as the broken arch, which first appeared about 1720. The term 'grandfather' is generally applied to clocks of 6 feet and over in height, and 'grandmother' to clocks of about 5 feet 6 inches and less; 17th century grandmother clocks are very rare.

It is quite impossible to suggest a value for this type of clock without individual details but a rough estimate would be from £10 up to £1,500 or £2,000 and by a eminent maker considerable more, £10,000 to £20,000.

Above:
Early Long Case Clock

Left:
Fully Developed Long Case Clock

Lyre Clock   1785

Of French manufacture, some lyre clocks were made with the pendulum suspended at the top of the case. The pendulum bob is in the form of a circle of pastes which surrounds the dial of the

Lyre Clock

clock, and swings from side to side outside the case. A most attractive clock.

The value of 19th century lyre clocks varies considerably, and depends on the quality of the case and the decorative value. A fair estimate would be anything from about £85 to say £1,500.

After the Revolution in France a lyre clock was developed in America as a simpler wall clock in wood with the clock dial on the top instead of in the middle of the 'lyre'.

M

Magic Lantern Clock   1850

Originally made in France, this is a form of night clock in which an image of the dial and hands of a clock are projected on to the wall.

Such clocks continued to be made in Germany well into the 19th century. The later models were made to project the image on to the ceiling. Of little value.

Magnetic Clock   1948

A truly magnetic clock where the pendulum is kept vibrating by magnetism. Invented by C. F. CLIFFORD of Bath, England. A feature of the clock is that it is completely silent and a precision timekeeper.

See TORTOISE AND MOUSE CLOCKS

Mains Clock 1918

Invented or discovered by Warren of the U.S.A. in 1918. A popular clock at the time of its introduction and for a long time after.

It is not a clock in the generally accepted sense of the term, but a synchronous alternating current motor which is controlled by the frequency of the generator at the electric power station. If for some reason the frequency alters or the power is cut, mains clocks are affected.

(a) The generator at the power station; (b) the clock at the power station; (c) the clock in the wall.

Suitable only where a.c. is available.

Sometimes referred to as 'synchronous clocks'.

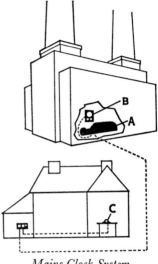

Mains Clock System

Mantle Clock

A clock made to stand on a mantle-piece, another name for BRACKET CLOCK (q.v.).

Marble Clocks 1885

The term marble clock usually refers to the black 'marble' type of clock illustrated, but in fact the cases of these clocks are made of slate.

Marble clocks are usually of French make with pendulum movements and their virtue is that they are heavy and not easily moved.

There are numerous types of clocks with cases made of marble, but the

Marble Clock

marble forms the lesser part of the case. Marble or onyx has been used in the manufacture of clocks since the early 18th century, but the marble clock is from the last quarter of the 19th century.

Marble clocks are of little value at the present time and can be obtained for just a few pounds. Where marble or onyx forms the lesser part of the clock, the value could be similar to that of the BULL and LYRE CLOCKS (q.v.).

Marine Chronometer

Another name for BOX CHRONOMETER (q.v.).

Marine Clock

See SHIP's CLOCK and SHIP's BELL CLOCK.

Master Clock   1900

The term Master clock refers to a clock which controls by electric impulse a number of impulse dial clocks. The impulse dial clock is not a clock in itself, but a simple mechanism in which an electrical impulse causes a step forward action, with suitable gearing to indicate hours minutes and seconds.

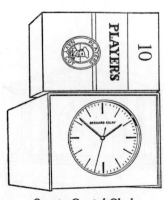

Quartz Crystal Clock

Micro Quartz Clock   1964

One name for a miniaturised electronic chronometer about the size of a packet of ten cigarettes. Such instruments are extremely accurate. The time base is provided by a quartz crystal. See QUARTZ CRYSTAL CLOCK.

74

Minute Repeating Clocks   1870

These clocks are of Swiss manufacture
and the principle of their construction is
similar to a repeating pocket watch. The
clock itself is a timepiece, and by
depressing a button, usually placed at the
top of the case, the repeating mainspring
is wound so that the correct hours,
quarters and minutes are struck.

Such clocks are usually small, about
2½ inches high, in silver and silver
enamelled cases. A great number was
made by Mathey Tissot.

There are also carriage clocks with
minute repeating work.

A carriage minute repeating clock
could be worth about £200 to £300
depending on its quality, etc.

The small clocks mentioned above are
worth from about £85 to £150. However, in estimating the value of these
clocks, it should be borne in mind that
much depends on the quality of the
movement and the case.

See also CARRIAGE CLOCK.

Monastery Clock   1450

An early form of alarm clock used in
monastries to give warning to a monk to
ring a bell to summon to prayer or duties.

The clock is not a clock in the accepted
sense of the term, but an alarm. The dial
has holes drilled around it, in which a
peg is placed. As the dial rotates, the
projecting peg releases the handle of the
alarm weight mechanism and the bell is
rung until the weight runs down.

It would be the duty of the clock-
keeper to set and wind the weight up
ready for the next alarm warning which
indicated when to sound the prayer bell
by hand.

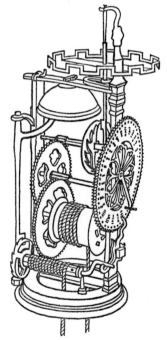

Monastery Clock

Monstrance Clock 1600

A clock on the form of a monstrance used in Roman Catholic Churches. These clocks made of brass, gilt, are usually of German make and stand about 8 to 10 inches tall. Many were made in Augsburg.

Monstrance clocks are rare and their value varies considerably, from about £500 to £1,000 or more.

Monstrance Clock

Morbier Clock 1750

Clocks made in the village of Morbier, near Morez, in the Department of Jura, adjoining France-Comte, France. A feature of these clocks is the upright rack of the striking mechanism. Also known as 'Comtoise clocks'.

Morbier clocks are often to be seen in Eastern France and Switzerland, the dial giving the name and address of the vendor. The name 'Morbier' only rarely appears on the movement or dial.

The clocks were either longcase or lantern with long pendulum. Originally they had VERGE ESCAPEMENTS (q.v.) and subsequently ANCHOR ESCAPEMENTS (q.v.).

The value is similar to that of DUTCH CLOCKS (q.v.).

Mouse Clock 1650

Invented by the redoubtable Grollier (see notes under INCLINED PLANE CLOCK). Wood, in his 'Curiosities of Clocks and Watches' makes a brief mention of it but there seems to be no record of such a contrivance in existence.

The principle is that a model of a mouse travels round the cornice of a room, being propelled magnetically. It

is reasonable to conceive that a model
of a mouse fixed to a chain could be
made to travel round a room, once in
24 hours, say on the picture rail, suitably
marked to indicate the time of day. The
chain could be operated by a simple
8 day movement.

Moving Eye Clock

See NEGRO CLOCK.

Musical Clocks   1750

Both English and continental musical
clocks were made, including BRACKET
(q.v.) and LONGCASE (q.v.) clocks, which
at pre-determined times, usually every
three hours, played tunes upon bells.

A pin barrel is employed to operate
the hammers. Some clocks are provided
with a repertoire of tunes, e.g. gavottes,
dances, etc., with changes on the same
barrel. Others are provided with a set
of barrels so that the entire barrel can
be changed, the spare barrels being
stored in a drawer at the base of the
clock.

In recent years the Swiss have produced musical alarm clocks incorporating small musical units operating on a
comb, such as would be used in musical
boxes. The music part is wound in the
normal manner, as one would wind an
alarm clock.

An 18th century English bracket
musical clock could be worth from £350
to £1,500, depending upon its size,
quality, etc. A longcase clock would be
worth a little less.

Mystery Clocks   1850

The illustration is one version of many
types of mystery clock. The same principle is employed in each. That shown
is of French make and fine quality. The

Mystery Clock

77

mechanism is in the base which is of wood with ormolu mounts. The centre column comprises a clear glass tube with a solid clear glass rod running through the centre.

To the lower end is fixed a gear connected to the mechanism, to the top end a gear also is fixed which gears through one of the supporting pieces to the teeth of a wheel fixed to the periphery of a circular plate of glass, to which the hand is fitted. The glass plate rotates and with it the hand to indicate the time of day.

Also see MYSTERY LADY CLOCK.

A novelty clock, the one illustrated could be worth £100 or more.

Mystery Lady Clock

Mystery Lady Clock   1875

There are two types of clock which bear this description. In the first of these, the figure stands stationary and the clock movement is fitted with a short bob pendulum which banks between two pins fixed to the back plate of the movement. When the whole pendulum is set swinging the impact of the inner pendulum on one of the banking pins provides the necessary impulse to keep the pendulum oscillating. The whole mechanism is driven by a mainspring in the conventional manner.

The second (illustrated) is a clock in which both the figure and the pendulum it holds comprise the pendulum and part of the escapement. The figure is fixed to the platform upon which it stands and it is the platform which twists, as it were, very slightly and the swing of the pendulum controls the movement. The twist is so slight, first one way and then the other, that it is not discernable.

78

The value is similar to that of the
MYSTERY CLOCK (q.v.). During the
latter part of the 18th century a great
number of a cheap variety were made
in Germany. Their value now is just a
few pounds.

N

Napoleon Clock   1900

Refers to the style of case, taking its
name from the style of hat worn by
Napoleon.
Clocks of this type were made in large
quantities between 1900–1938, often of
very poor quality, both in the case and
the movement.

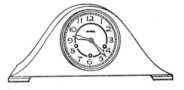

Napoleon Clock

Nef Clock   1875

A clock which is incorporated in a
model of a ship, usually a galleon.
Although the clock is associated with a
ship it is not a SHIP'S CLOCK (q.v.).
In evaluating the value of a Nef clock,
a great deal depends upon the case
which is by far the more valuable part
of the clock.
There is also a clock where a figure
of a helmsman rocks backwards and
forwards with the swing of the pendulum
could be worth about £150.

Negro Clock

Early German automaton clock. A ball shaped clock with a band round its circumference with the hours marked upon it. The ball is mounted on a post to resemble a palm tree. A negro with a stick in his hand stands and points to the time of day. At the hours, the negro turns his head and the dog attempts to jump.

Another negro clock is a model of the head and bust of a negress. The eyes indicate the time, the left eyeball having the hours marked upon it and the right eyeball, the minutes. The time is read in a similar way to the TICKET and the DIGITAL CLOCKS (q.v.). These are of French make, and one such clock is in Buckingham Palace, London.

In more recent years (about 1900), a cheaper version was produced, showing a negro with the hours painted round the left eye, and the right eye treated in a similar manner but indicating minutes. The eyeballs rotated, a mark on each indicating hours and minutes. The figure made of wood, was gaily painted and fitted with a 30 hour movement.

Low quality German negro clocks of about 1890 are worth about £20 to £35, whereas a negress head clock of fine quality French make could be worth as much as £1,500 or even more.

Neuchateloise Clock

Neuchateloise Clock   1950

A style of clock, made in Switzerland, but in form a copy of the French Louis XVI clocks.

Neuchateloise clocks are still made by three or four manufacturers in Switzerland. The cases are of wood, lacquered and decorated with flowers either in colour or gilt.

The movement is usually 8 day ting-tang quarter striking with pendulum. A feature of these clocks is the corbel bracket which is made and decorated in the same manner as the clock case.

The illustration on the facing page is a typical example.

Night Clock   1685

A clock in which the dial is lighted up as distinct from a luminous dial where a luminous compound is employed.

There are many forms of night clocks but basically the principle is for a light—candle, oil lamp, etc.—to shine through an aperture from behind an opaque dial so that the figures and the hands are visible at night.

The illustration is of a 17th century longcase clock by East. The clock illustrated under LAMP CLOCK (q.v.) is of a more modern conception of a night clock of French manufacture, and the principle is a little different. The globe which forms the dial revolves, and a fixed point on the case indicates the time.

A night clock like that illustrated here could be worth £3,000 to £5,000 but there are many cheap versions, usually of German make, worth only a few pounds.

Night Clock

O

Oil Clock

See LAMP CLOCK.

One Wheel Clock   1750

Invented by Pierre le Roy about 1750, this clock has one wheel only to the actual clock mechanism. This wheel

One Wheel Clock

81

forms the train and escape wheel to keep the pendulum vibrating. The dial is of glass so that the mechanism can be seen.

It is an exhibition piece of exquisite workmanship and ingenuity and serves no special purpose except to display the genius of the person who devised it.

An example of this clock is to be seen in the Ilbert collection, in the British Museum, London.

A one-wheel clock is very rare and could be valued at from £1,000 to £2,000 or even more.

Organ Clock   1750

A pipe organ operated by a pin barrel similar to that used in a musical clock, or box. The clock part releases the organ at three-hourly intervals—sometimes less frequently. The wind is supplied by bellows in the conventional manner.

Organ clocks are uncommon and are to be found as bracket clocks, about 18 inches high. More rarely, they were made as large clocks, standing 4 to 5 feet high. In addition to the organ, cymbals, bells and drums are sounded.

They were much favoured in Eastern countries.

Because of the variety of organ clocks, the remarks made about the LONGCASE and MUSICAL CLOCKS (q.v.) could apply. The value would be in the region of £1,500.

Ormolu Clock   1675

The term 'ormolu' refers to the all metal gilt clock cases of the late 17th century to the end of the 19th century.

Ormolu means gold ground to powder (*or moulu*) and amalgamated with mercury

Organ Clock

82

and applied to the metal, a form of gilding.

Ormolu is now understood to refer to brass castings which have been gilt and used as decoration on clock cases, and also to complete cases.

Orrery Clock   1715

A mechanical device consisting of a number of spheres mounted on rods or stems, each sphere representing one of the heavenly bodies. The spheres traverse in orbits round a common centre which represents the sun.

The contrivance is activated by the clock mechanism and illustrates the relative sizes, positions and motions— not distances—of bodies rotating round the sun; i.e. the earth and the planets.

An orrery is a mechanical platetarium, and can be made to operate either mechanically, or manually as a separate instrument.

The name 'orrery' is taken from the 4th Earl of Orrery for whom one of the earliest orrerie was made in 1715. The Earl of Orrery was the patron of John Rowley the famous scientific instrument maker of Fleet Street, London, a close neighbour of Tompion, and probably the first orrery was made by Rowley.

Orrery clocks are very rare and the value varies considerably. A fair estimate would be anything from £1,000 to £3,000 or more.

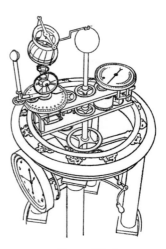

Orrery Clock

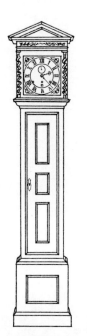

Pediment Top Clock

Pendule D'Officier Clock

P

Pedestal Clock

See Column Clock.

Pediment Top Clock   1660

Refers to a clock case where the top is in the form of a sloping roof, also known as Architectural (q.v.). First appeared about the middle of the 17th century. The illustration is of an early longcase clock with pediment hood. The term also refers to the top of a barometer and alternatively described as 'swan neck'.

For value see Architectural Top Clock.

Pendule d'Officier Clock   1780

Originally a form of portable clock devised by the famous maker A. L. Breguet and used by Napoleon and his officers. Now a French desk clock. The illustration shows a typical example, fitted with a striking movement, Verge Escapement (q.v.) in an ormolu case, with white enamel dial. These clocks generally run for from three to five days at one winding.

It is possible that the style of clock was the fore-runner of the French Carriage Clock (q.v.).

The value can be assessed at between £250 and £500. If by Breguet could be very much more.

Perpetual Calendar Clock

With the ordinary calendar clock it is necessary to change the date manually at the termination of the month when there are not 31 days in the month. In other words the calendar will read to 31 days for all months.

The perpetual calendar clock automatically changes from say the 30th to the 1st, and 28th to the 1st, also on leap years it will automatically change from 29th February to 1st March.

In addition to the date such clocks show the month and the day of the week.

Some of the finest specimens were made by A. L. Breguet, the eminent French maker.

19th century perpetual calendar clocks of French make are worth from about £75 to £350 or more for a clock by an eminent maker.

Some LIGHT CLOCKS (q.v.) are fitted with perpetual date mechanism. This type of clock was introduced in 1964.

Petite Sonnerie Clock 1850

Usually a FRENCH CARRIAGE CLOCK (q.v.) which strikes TING-TANG (q.v.) at the quarters.

See GRANDE SONNERIE.

Value: See CARRIAGE CLOCKS.

Picture Clock 1750

A painting which includes a tower or steeple with a clock placed in the appropriate position. Usually such clocks are fitted with 30 hour verge watch movements, sometimes with an 8-day TIC-TAC (q.v.) pendulum movement.

Some of the older picture clocks can be valued at around £75 to £200. There are also modern versions of Swiss make sold at £30 to £40.

Picture Clock

Pigeon Clock 1900

A clock for the timing of racing pigeons. The clock illustrated is made by Henry Martens and Cie, Brussels,

Pigeon Clock

85

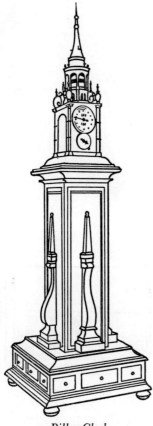

Pillar Clock

Belgium, and marketed by the Automatic Timing Clock Co., Ltd., Stacksteads, Bacup, Lancs, and known as Toulet Super. The original pigeon clock was invented by Turner.

The method of use is as follows—
Ten birds can be timed with this clock. Rings with either numbers or private marks are placed on a leg of each pigeon. The time is recorded at the release of the birds. As the birds arrive home, they are caught and the ring removed and placed in a thimble which is then inserted in a slot in the clock. A lever is depressed which prints on the paper the time of the insertion of the thimble. In this manner the times of arrival of the birds can be compared.

Pillar Clock   1590

The name given to a clock upon a pillar-like base, of German make, 3 ft high. May be the French emulated this style of case when designing their COLUMN CLOCK.

Value: Much depends on the quality of the case and the maker's name, but it could be from £350 to £2,000 or even more.

Pin Wheel Escapement   1750

Pin Wheel Escapement

Invented by the French horologist Amant 1749, the pin wheel escapement is a form of DEAD BEAT ESCAPEMENT (q.v.) much used by French clockmakers especially for TURRET CLOCKS (q.v.). An advantage of this escapement is that as the bearing holes of the arbor, carrying the pallets become worn the correct action of the escapement is not seriously affected. Not to be confused with the pin pallet escapement used in lower priced clocks and watches.

Pistol Alarm 1700

An alarm once made in France and called a 'Reveil a' Pistolet'. The alarm clock fires a miniature cannon and lights a candle at the hour required.

One can be seen in the Musee des Beaux Arts, Besancon, France.

Planetary Clock 1700

A clock geared to show the motions of various planets on a special dial.

Plato Clock

An American term for a TICKET CLOCK (q.v.).

Portfolio Clock

See THREE FOLD CLOCK.

Postman's Alarm Clock 1850

A simple DIAL CLOCK (q.v.) which has wooden case and dial and no glass to cover the dial and hands. The clock is fitted with an alarm mechanism, and is pendulum controlled and weight driven. Made to hang on the wall.

The value of these clocks is low, only a few pounds.

Pull Quarter Clock 1670

A system found in 17th century clocks, in which, by pulling a cord, the time to within the nearest quarter hour will be sounded. The clocks are often timepieces only—non strike—but pull quarter mechanism is also to be found in striking clocks. They are furnished with a nest of 2, 4, or 6 bells, most usually 4 bells.

Value: See BRACKET CLOCK.

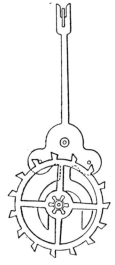

Pin Pallet Escapement

Q

Quail Clock

A version of the Cuckoo Clock (q.v.) but in place of or as well as the call of cuckoo, the call of the quail is employed.

Quarter Clock

Another name for Chime Clock (q.v.).

Quartz Crystal Clock   1929

W. A. Morrison of New York, U.S.A. investigated in 1929 the properties of quartz crystal and discovered that the vibrations or oscillations are practically constant in frequency when an A.C. is applied, so that quartz could be used as a time controller.

A brief description of the quartz crystal clock is as follows:—the frequency of the oscillations is controlled by a ring shaped piece of quartz crystal, of about 3 inches diameter. If kept at a constant temperature and if the valve circuits are electrically constant, the vibrations of the crystal will be constant.

If the frequency is, say, 100,000 cycles per second the effects of any variations in the supply voltage are reduced to a minimum. A submultiple regenerative dividor reduces this frequency to 1,000 per second. When the time recorder is a Synchronous Motor Clock (q.v.) the submultiple dividor reduces the frequency to 50 cycles per second. It is recorded that the accuracy of the quartz crystal is of the order of one-thousandth of a second in 24 hours, an accuracy of about one part in one hundred million.

See Micro-Quartz Clock.

R

Railway Clocks   1850

About the middle of the 19th century, clocks in railway stations were set to show local time. As the railway expanded it was necessary, for purposes of time tables, to regularize the time and Greenwich Mean Time was adopted.

Up to this time, leaflets giving conversion figures from local time to G.M.T. i.e. railway time, were issued. Local inhabitants still used local time.

Recital Clock

Recital Clock

An 8 day alarm clock which repeats the alarm every 24 hours without resetting.

Regulator

See ENGLISH REGULATOR CLOCK.

Religieuse Clock   1680–1700

Named after a nun in French, this is a simple form of clock with round chapter ring set on a dark background in a rectangular case with cresting. It is reminiscent in appearance to a nun in habit.

Religieuse clocks are rare and have no real market value. An estimate would be somewhere in the region of £100 to £250.

Religieuse Clock

89

Remontoire Clock 1750

Refers to a clock where the main source of power periodically winds a smaller mainspring or lifts a weight, which provides a constant force to the escapement.

A mainspring driven clock thus becomes weight-driven and therefore the force applied by the escapement is constant.

There are many versions of this principle.

Antique clocks fitted with this system are rare and their value depends to a considerable extent upon their importance. Generally £100 may be added to the values given for other clocks—bracket or longcase—not fitted with remontoire work.

Repeater Clock 1700

A clock which can be made to strike the previous hour, as with an ENGLISH BRACKET CLOCK (q.v.) in which a cord is pulled which releases the strike.

Also CARRIAGE CLOCK (q.v.) in which the striking is released by pressing a button.

VALUE: See BRACKET and CARRIAGE CLOCKS.

Revolution Clock

See EMPIRE CLOCK and DECIMAL DIAL CLOCK.

Riefler Clock 1893

Refers to an ASTRONOMICAL REGULATOR (q.v.) type of clock invented by Sigmund Riefler of Germany.

The special features of this clock are the escapement and the pendulum. Impulse is given to the pendulum by the

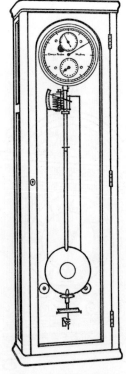

Riefler Pendulum Clock

flexing of the pendulum suspension spring. The theory is that the period vibration of the pendulum is consiquently not affected by variations in the motive power. The conventional method of impulse is through the crutch, which acts directly upon the pendulum rod at each swing, so that variations of power cause some disturbance, however slight.

The Riefler pendulum is compensated for changes in temperature. The rod is of nickel steel and the bob rests on a short tube of aluminium, calculated to compensate for the small coefficient of expansion of the rod.

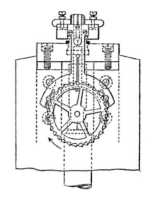

Riefler Escapement

It is interesting to note that Riefler patented his system of imparting impulse to the pendulum in 1893, and there is in Buckingham Palace, London, a clock made by Breguet in 1823 which has a pin wheel escapement with impulse to the pendulum by flexing the suspension spring.

A German Riefler clock could be worth about £100 to £200 and the Breguet clock £5,000 to £10,000 or even more.

Roman Strike Clock   1685

Refers to the system of striking the hours according to the Roman numerals.

The system was first used by Joseph Knibb, and the idea was to conserve power. Such clocks are fitted with two bells, one of high and one of low tone. The low note indicates the figure V and the high note the figure 1; two low notes indicate X.

The table gives the sequence of striking.

o'clock
1 (I)   one blow on high note
2 (II)   two blows on high note

3 (III)	three blows on high note
4 (IV)	one on high note and one on low note
5 (V)	one on low note
6 (VI)	one on low note and one on high note
7 (VII)	one on low note and two on high note
8 (VIII)	one on low note and three on high note
9 (IX)	one on high note and two on low note
10 (X)	two on low note
11 (XI)	two on low note and one on high note
12 (XII)	two on low note and two on high note

With Roman strike 30 blows are struck in 12 hours as compared with 78 blows with the conventional striking.

A Knibb Roman strike clock could be worth from £3,500 to £5,000 or even more.

Rope Clock

See VILLARD'S ROPE ESCAPEMENT.

S

Seticon Clock   1960

A battery-driven clock using the Universal Escapement Co's movement, made in Switzerland.

A continuously running transistorised motor drives the clock and also operates a REMONTOIRE (q.v.) which provides constant force to a form of CHRONO-METER ESCAPEMENT (q.v.).

Sectronic Clock   1963

A battery-driven clock with a special movement made by Smiths called the 'Sectronic'.

A coil of wire on the balance is supplied with pulses of electrical energy

Seticon Clock

which keep the balance swinging to and fro to drive the clock hands. Switching is by transistor but the rate of the balance controls the timekeeping.

Battery clocks with transistor are made by several other manufacturers of battery clocks abroad.

Sedan Clock   1750

Sedan, a town in France, a centre of watchmaking in the 16th century. It is recorded that the Sedan chair originated here and was introduced into England by James 1, 1603–1625, but it was not in general use until the 18th century. There is however no evidence that these clocks were used in sedan chairs, but the name persists.

The cases were made of wood or metal, circular, square with cut corners, or octagonal, and about 6 inches across, and were fitted with 30 hour verge watch movements.

The value of a sedan clock depends on the case but can be anything from about £15 to £35.

Sevres Clock

Refers to the case of the clock, made of Sevres (France) china. Usually fitted with a French movement.

A genuine Sevres china clock can be worth several thousand pounds.

Sheep's Head Clock   1650

A LANTERN CLOCK (q.v.) with an extended hour zone, as illustrated. The name is presumed to have been given because of the resemblance to the head-on view of a sheep's head.

Value: See LANTERN CLOCK.

Sedan Clock

Sheep's Head Clock

Shelf Clock

Shelf Clock 1810

The American term for a BRACKET CLOCK (q.v.), but with particular reference to the style of clock as illustrated.

Many of these clocks have low quality pendulum movements, ribbon or strip pallets—not solid—and pierced plates. The mainsprings are free, not enclosed in barrels, and the clocks usually strike the hours and half hours upon a large spiral wire gong, secured to the back of the case.

The first shelf clocks were made by Eli Terry and Eli Whitney and the main part of the mechanism was of wood. About 1837, rolled brass was employed and with it came the introduction of mass production.

Although made down to a price, vast numbers are still giving good service in the U.S.A. and occasionally they are to be found in England.

The illustration is of a reproduction of a Terry shelf clock made by the CHELSEA CLOCK CO. (q.v.).

The values of shelf clocks vary very much. They can be worth anything from about £10 to £150 or even more if made by Terry or other eminent maker.

Ship's Bell Clock 1850

A clock similar in appearance to a SHIP'S CLOCK (q.v.). It strikes the time at each half hour to denote 'watches' e.g. at 12.30 a.m. and p.m. one note is sounded and is termed 'one bell', at 1 a.m. and p.m. two blows and called 'two bells' and so on, up to 4 a.m. and p.m. when eight bells is sounded.

The double notes are sounded in quick succession, like the ting-tang, but on the same bell: e.g. at 1 a.m. and p.m. *ting-ting* and at 4 a.m. and p.m. *ting-ting—ting-ting—ting-ting—ting-ting.*

Ship's Chronometer

See Box Chronometer.

Ship's Clock

A simple timepiece clock with lever escapement, usually fitted into a round brass case with a flange to enable it to be screwed on to a bulkhead or panel. Also known as a marine clock.

Ship's Clock

Shortt Free Pendulum   1910

Invented by W. H. Shortt, the free pendulum (it is not a clock in its own right) is an astronomical precision instrument and was adapted to the Synchronome Clock system of Master Clock (q.v.) and slave clock.

The free pendulum is encased in a copper cylinder with a domed glass top and is completely air tight, so that the cylinder can be almost exhausted of air. The air pressure is kept constant at 30mm of mercury.

The accuracy is of the order of one part in three hundred million or about 1/10th of a second per year or 1 second in 10 years, that is after allowing for predictable errors in the earth's rotation, such as nutation.

Skeleton Clock   1860

A clock movement with the plates pierced out to expose the mechanism, usually of English manufacture but Continental examples are to be found and the style probably originated in France.

The English clocks generally strike just one stroke at each hour, but full striking and chiming clocks are to be found. The movement is fixed to a plinth and covered with a glass shade.

Nineteenth century English skeleton clocks are worth from £25 to about £150.

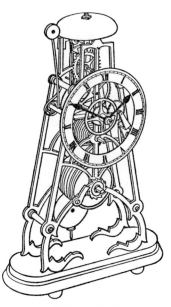

Skeleton Clock

A dial showing the time but without a clock movement of its own. Instead it is controlled, usually with a number of other slave clocks in a building, by a central MASTER CLOCK (q.v.).

Speaking Clock   1936

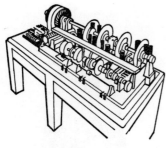

Speaking Clock

Also known as 'Tim'. If the letters TIM (or now 123) are dialled on the telephone, the Speaking Clock, housed at the Post Office Research Station, Dollis Hill, London, N.W., will announce the exact time; e.g. at, say, 10 minutes past 10 o'clock it will say 'at the third stroke it will be ten-ten and ten seconds' followed by three pips, and so on.

While in Paris in 1933, G.P.O. officials became interested in the speaking clock just inaugurated in that city. After consideration it was decided to develop a similar system in this country. This work was entrusted to Dr. E. A. Speight, who devised an entirely new system employing a free pendulum as the time control.

A 24 hour service is available and the error is never greater than 1/10th of a second; the system was brought into service on the afternoon of July 24th, 1936.

Staartklok

See FRIESLAND CLOCK.

Stage Coach Clock   1760

These clocks, used in inns which were the stopping places of stage coaches, were usually black with bright reds, blues, and yellows as decoration. They had bold dial with no glass covering, and they were the fore-runners of the ACT OF PARLIAMENT CLOCK (q.v.).

Value: Anything from £15 to £100.

Stoeltjesklok

See FRIESLAND CLOCK and ZAANDAM CLOCK.

Striking Jack Clock   1382

Early TURRET CLOCKS (q.v.) were not fitted with dials and hands; they struck the hours etc. only. At a later date, 1380, figures of men were employed to strike the bells. For example, on clocks which struck the quarter hours, two figures would be employed, each holding a hammer, with either a twisting movement of the whole body, a lifting of the arms, these were made by the clock to strike the bells.

Usually these figures, known as striking jacks, were housed inside the building.

Stage Coach Clock

Strut Clock   1920

Refers to a clock with a strut hinged at the back of the case to enable the clock to stand at an angle, as would an easel. Usually such clocks are small, 3 to 4 inches high, but some up to 7 or 8 inches are to be found.

This style of clock is now superseded by the folding type of travelling clock.

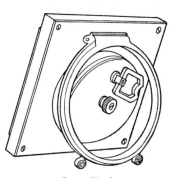

Strut Clock

97

Sunburst Clock

See SUNRAY CLOCK.

Sun Ray Clock

Sunray Clock   1860

Also known as 'sunburst clocks'. The style of the case originated in Italy *circa* 1750, but it was used as a frame for a mirror or plaque.

About 1850 it appeared in England with a French DRUM (q.v.) movement but it did not become popular until the first quarter of the 20th century.

The cases are gesso work, i.e. carved wood treated with plaster of Paris and then gilt with gold leaf. The cheaper versions are of plaster sprayed with gold paint.

Swing Clock   1890

A French made clock of good quality. A girl seated on a swing which swings to and fro, and not from side to side, as a conventional pendulum. A special form of anchor escapement is used and the swing forms the pendulum.

In the Black Forest of Germany, a cheaper version is made in the form of a miniature cuckoo clock with a girl on a spring which bobs up and down. This forms the pendulum.

This is a novelty clock. The French models can be valued at around £35 and the lower quality German clocks at a pound or two.

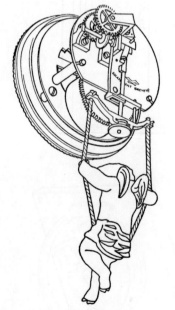

Swing Clock

Synchronome Clock   1895

The word Synchronome—the name of the firm of makers—has become synonymous with a type of MASTER CLOCK, (q.v.). It is an electric seconds

98

pendulum clock which can operate a great number of subsidiary or SLAVE DIALS (q.v.). The clock was invented by F. Hope-Jones in 1895.

It is this clock which became the slave to the FREE PENDULUM (q.v.).

The prime object was, and still is, to operate a system of subsidiary dials. The master clock is fitted with a seconds pendulum which receives impulse by the weight of a falling lever which is released mechanically every 30 seconds and is returned to its zero position by an electro-magnet. The Synchronome clock is approximately a 'free pendulum' in its own right and the SHORTT FREE PENDULUM (q.v.) is a refinement of it.

Synchronous Clock

See MAINS CLOCK.

T

Table Clocks   1500

The introduction of the mainspring, attributed (probably falsely) to Peter Henlein, about 1511, made clocks portable. Previously all clocks were weight-driven and therefore not portable.

The illustration is of the earliest known spring-driven clock, made by Jacob the Czech 1525, who is said to have invented the FUSEE (q.v.), a device to equalise the force or the power of the mainspring. Leonardo da Vinci illustrated the fusee in one of his notebooks just before 1500. No doubt Jacob the Czech put the idea into practice.

Clocks of this form were made well into the 17th century. All the clocks had an hour hand only, and no glass covering.

The value of these clocks can vary tremendously, anything from say £200 to £3,000 or even more.

See VERTICAL TABLE CLOCK.

Table Clock

99

Tambour Clock 1900

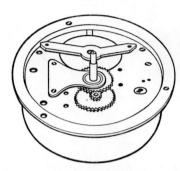

Tambour Clock

This name refers to a small Drum (q.v.) form of clock—usually Swiss—which is screwed to a case; a Tambour consists of a movement, generally key-wind, and a metal case with no dial or bezel. Often the same size as a Calotte (q.v.) but made for a different purpose.

Tape Chronograph

An instrument used to compare the rates of clocks, watches, chronometers, star transits and other timekeeping methods. A simple type consists of a moving paper tape marked by two pens. Each timekeeper being compared causes a pen to make a mark at, say, the hour. From the difference in the positions of the marks, the differences in rate can be calculated.

Tavern Clock 1790

See Act of Parliament and Stage Coach Clock.

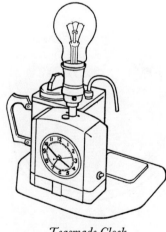

Teasmade Clock

Tea Time Clock

An alarm clock fitted into a fixture comprising an electric kettle and a teapot. At the required hour, the clock switches on the electric power, the water boils and is poured into the teapot to make the tea, the alarm sounds and an electric light is switched on.

The clock illustrated is made by Goblin.

Tell-Tale Clock

Another name for Watchman's Clock (q.v.).

Tellurion Clock 1765

(Lat: tellus-uris earth.)

A clock of either French or Swiss make, which has what looks like an orrery type of mechanism surmounting the clock, but which in fact shows the succession of the day and night and changes of seasons.

Tellurion clocks made by Francois Ducommun, of Chaux-de-Fonds, Switzerland, are to be seen in the Neuchâtel and Chaux-de-Fonds museums. One depicts the earth with a scale for the ages of the moon, and a revolving scale showing month and four-yearly calendar. Also indicating day and night and Spring, summer, autumn, and winter.

See ORRERY CLOCK.

Value: From £1,000 to £3,000 and even more, depending on the maker's name, etc.

Term Clock 1720

A kind of trunk, pillar or pedestal clock, sometimes in the form of an inverted obelisk, as the illustration. The pedestal is small at the base increasing upwards in size, upon which a clock is fixed. Much used by the French and occasionally by the English.

See COLUMN CLOCK.

Value: From £350 to £2,000, but much depends on the quality of the case and the maker's name.

Thermograph Clock

A clock similar to the BAROGRAPH (q.v.) but in place of the aneroid, a bi-metallic strip, or other device, is used, to register changes of temperature upon a chart.

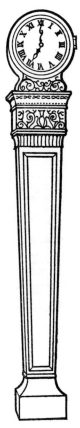

Term Clock

Three Fold Clock

Tic-Tac Escapement

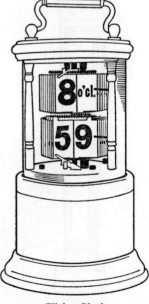

Ticket Clock

Three Fold Clock 1900

A popular type of travel clock. Also known as 'portfolio clock' which appeared about the beginning of the 20th century. A development of the GOLIATH CLOCK (q.v.), they consist of a CALOTTE (q.v.) fitted into a leather case, usually with a Swiss movement, running for 30 hours or 8 days, often with alarm mechanism.

Tic-Tac Escapement 1670

A form of ANCHOR ESCAPEMENT (q.v.) used by some of the old master clock-makers about 1670–80.

The pallets embrace two teeth only and when used with a short pendulum the arc is relatively small.

The tic-tac escapement is rare in 17th century clocks, The VERGE ESCAPEMENT (q.v.) was more favoured.

About 1850, the French produced DRUM CLOCKS (q.v.) in large quantities with tic-tac escapements. The illustration is of a French version. The English 17th century escapement was the same in principle but with slightly different shaped teeth and pallets.

Ticket Clock 1890

Sometimes referred to as 'Flick clock'. In this form of clock, the time is indicated by tickets or tablets which are released one at each minute to reveal the time of day e.g. 12–45; 12–46 and so on.

Large numbers of these clocks were made in France and Germany and sold during the 20th century. Digital read-out is becoming popular in electric and electronic clocks. See DIGITAL CLOCK.

The low quality German clock referred to is worth only a pound or two.

TIM

See SPEAKING CLOCK.

Time Recorder Clock   1910

A system employed to check the time
'in and out' of personnel of a factory,
office etc. Time recorder clocks are in
use in which the timekeeping mechanism
is spring-driven, but in recent years
such clocks are made with mains synchronous mechanism, or with spring-
driven mechanism electrically wound,
thus avoiding inconvenience of power
cuts.

The clock illustrated is made by
Smiths.

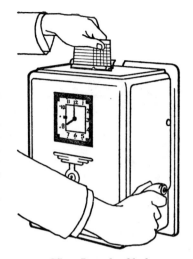

Time Recorder Clock

Time Recording Stamping Clock
1880

A hand date stamp which also shows
a clock dial with moving hand operated
by a built-in 30-hour clock. It is used
with an inking pad for stamping this
information on incoming correspond-
ence etc. to show time of arrival. Made
by the Warwick Time Stamp Company.

Ting-Tang Quarter Clock   1875

A clock which strikes four double notes
preceeding the hour striking, and one
double note at the quarter past, two at
the half hour, and three at quarter to
the hour.

Usually there are two winding squares,
but there are instances where one winding square winds the whole clock
mechanism, including the timekeeping
part.

Known on the continent as 'Bim-
Bam'.

Time Recording Stamp Clock

Torsion Clock

See FOUR-HUNDRED DAY CLOCK.

Tortoise Clock

This was invented by Grollier de Servière, and consists of a dish of water with a model of a tortoise (or turtle) floating upon the water. The tortoise is made to swim around the dish in 12 hours by means of a magnet fitted to the clock mechanism and a piece of iron attached to the tortoise. The hours are indicated around the rim of the dish.

Tortoise clocks are made at the present time, some with the plate or dish mounted on very attractive stands.

They are also known as turtle clocks.

A modern reproduction tortoise clock can be valued at from £35 to about £85.

Tortoise Clock

Tower Clock

Another name for TURRET CLOCK (q.v.).

Transistorised Clock   1960

A battery-driven clock employing a transistor, which makes use of the properties of contact between metal and a semi-conductor, and acts as an amplifier and an oscillator. The movement of the clock illustrated on page 92 is driven by a transistorised motor. Transistorised balance wheel, transistorised pendulum, and transistorised tuning fork clocks are also made.

See SELTICON CLOCK.

Travel Clocks

See CAMERA and THREE FOLD CLOCKS.

Trumpeter Clock

A form of CUCKOO CLOCK (q.v.) which in place of the cuckoo appearing through the door a trumpeter appears and plays a tune.

A product of the Black Forest.

Tabular Chime Clock   1870

A CHIMING CLOCK (q.v.) in which tubes are employed in place of bells, gongs, or rods. Tubes can be used only in longcase clocks as a rule, owing to their length.

A good second hand tubular chime clock of English make can be worth anything from £100 to £500 or £600.

Turret Clock   1364–1400

A clock made for use in a turret or tower. The illustration is of the Salisbury Cathedral clock made about 1386 and considered to be the oldest surviving clock still working. When found it had an ANCHOR ESCAPEMENT (q.v.). The original escapement would have been the VERGE (q.v.) with foliot, as the pendulum was not invented until 1656. The escapement has now been converted back to verge with foliot.

The second illustration is of a modern turret clock, made by Messrs. E. Dent, of London, the makers of the Westminster clock.

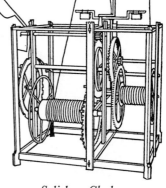

Salisbury Clock

*Turret
Clock*

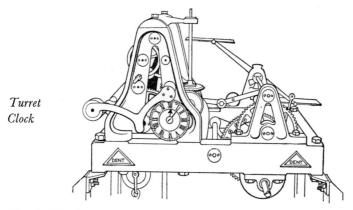

Turtle Clock

See TORTOISE CLOCK.

Urn or Vase Clock

U

Universal Clock

See WORLD TIME CLOCK.

Urn Clock   1750

These clocks are usually of French manufacture. The case takes the form of an urn or vase and the time of day is indicated by rotating band dials, one for the hours and one for the minutes.

Some fixed form of decoration e.g. an arrow or the head of a snake, points to the time of day.

The illustration is a typical example, and the value could be from £750 to £1,500, depending upon the quality of the case, decoration, etc.

V

V.A.P. Clock   1850

A French drum clock made by Valonge à Paris. The initials stamped on the plate of the clock form a trade mark. The clocks are well made, some being fitted with the TIC-TAC escapement (q.v.) and short bob pendulum.

Others are fitted with a unique form of lever escapement, robust and efficient. The escape wheel and lever are fitted between the plates with the rest of the train. The lever itself operates on the outside of the back plate and engages with the balance, which is held in position on a small separate platform or plate by the balance cock.

The drum complete fits into various styles of cases. One form is a drum fitted with two feet and ring at the top and sometimes with alarm mechanism.

Verge Escapement 1300

The earliest form of escapement in general use. It is not at present known who invented it. The verge escapement was in general use up to about 1800 first with foliot, balance wheel, and bar balance, then with pendulum.

The advantage of the verge escapement is that it is rugged. The clock can be moved about without fear of damage and it is not particular about being 'in beat'. The disadvantage is that it requires a wide angle of operation and is therefore not very suitable when a long pendulum is used.

The ANCHOR ESCAPEMENT (q.v.) is used when a long pendulum is employed.

Also referred to as 'crown wheel escapement'.

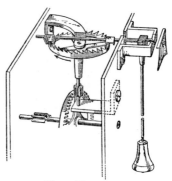

Verge Escapement

Vernis Martin Clock 1730

This term refers to the finish of a clock case similar in appearance to Japanese lacquer. Martin, a French cabinet maker, was the first to introduce this system of decoration, prior to French polishing.

Vernis (Fr. *Varnish*) is applied to a wood surface, first as a plain colour, green blue, red etc. and floral designs are painted upon the surface.

The form of decoration has become known as Vernis Martin and if the subject is a clock case, then it is called a 'vernis martin clock'.

That in the illustration is described as a vernis martin and ormolu mounted clock. The movement was made by another person.

The clock illustrated, which is of French- make, is worth £250 to £350.

Vernis Martin Clock

Vertical Table Clock

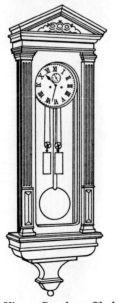

Vertical Table Clock   1530

These clocks are of German make and the mechanism is similar to the TABLE CLOCK (q.v.) but with certain complications, e.g. calendar work, solar time, etc. The illustration is a typical example and the value would be from £250 to £1,000 and an exceptional clock with complications from £5,000 to £7,500.

Vienna Regulator   1875

A weight-driven pendulum clock to hang on the wall. Made in Austria and Germany. Fitted with timepiece and striking movements, weight driven, usually with a wood rod pendulum, which is shorter than a seconds pendulum. Fitted with 'seconds' hand and separate dial, or sometimes centre seconds, but in view of the length of the pendulum, the 'seconds' hand does not indicate true seconds on some clocks.

Original Vienna regulators are not common and may be priced up to about £200. Most are of little value, from say £5 to £25.

Villard's Rope Escapement   1240–
1251

The first escapement recorded. There is no record of a clock fitted with this escapement, the device is noted in an architectural work by Villard or Wilars of Honnecourt, near Cambrai, France.

The device may well have prompted the inventor of the novelty clock illustrated. The cord winds round one post and then the other, being impelled by the main spindle to which the cord is attached; this spindle is driven by the clock work mechanism with which it is connected.

The common name for the type of clock described is the 'flying pendulum clock'. It was made during the last quarter of the 19th century and is now being made again as a novelty in Germany.

Visible Escapement Clock   1850

Usually refers to a French striking clock in which the escapement is visible from the front.

The Brocot escapement, invented by Achille Brocot of Paris, about 1750, was ideal for this purpose. The value is from about £25 to £50. The illustration under FOUR GLASS REGULATOR shows a typical example.

See BROCOT CLOCK.

Flying Pendulum Clock

W

Wag-on-the-Wall Clock

An American term for a WALL CLOCK (q.v.). Frequently fitted with a seconds pendulum. Both the weights and the pendulum are exposed.

Wagon Spring Clock   1825

A clock in which in place of a coiled mainspring a leaf spring is employed, as used in cars, wagons, etc. Invented by Joseph Ives, U.S.A. This system is to be found only in American clocks, and versions gave going times of 30 hours, 8 days, and 30 days.

There were six Ives brothers famous in early American clockmaking. Brooks Palmer, in his 'American Clock Book', lists some 20 Ives or combinations in various firms, so the Ives impact upon clock production could easily be the greatest of any one family in the U.S.A.

Wagon spring clocks are of American interest and are rare. Values can be assessed at from £150 to £300.

Wagon Spring

Wall Clock

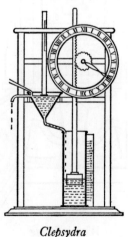

Clepsydra

Wall Clocks 1665

Table and lantern clocks are of the pre-pendulum era and it would be a natural development to encase the mechanism and the dial and hands completely.

The illustration is of a wall clock made by Edward East *circa* 1665 and is the earliest known 8-day clock made with a case of wood. Some wall clocks with cases of wood date from about 1660, but with 30 hour lantern clock mechanism. The value of the East clock would be about £5,000 or even more.

The next development was to encase the weights, and this is the first appearance of the longcase or GRANDFATHER CLOCK (q.v.).

The term wall clock refers to any clock made to hang on the wall e.g. CARTEL (q.v.) and DIAL CLOCK (q.v.).

Watchman's Clock 1750

Invented by Whitehurst of Derby. The clock consisted of a large rotating disc operated by a clock movement. Projecting pegs round the edge of the disc were pushed in by the watchman causing a record of the time of his visit to be made by the position of the altered pegs.

The modern version is a small portable clock which the watchman carries. At certain points of his visit a key chained to a fixture—a different key at each station—is inserted in the clock and a record is made of the time of his visit on a paper disc which is sealed in the clock.

Water (Clepsydra) Clock 1500 B.C.

The earliest means of time recording during the hours of darkness or when the sun was not shining. During the sunlight hours shadow clocks or sundials would be used.

The illustration is of a partly mechanical clepsydra clock and the method of operation is apparent. There is no known original example extant, and the information is gleaned from ancient records.

Weather Clock

See BAROGRAPH.

Westminster Clock

See BIG BEN.

World Time Clock   1930

A clock showing the times in various parts of the world, e.g. capitals of countries.

There are many systems to obtain the desired result. The one illustrated here is made by Luxor, Switzerland, and first appeared about 1930.

As an example; if the time is 9 a.m. in London, the outer ring is turned so that the London—Madrid—Algier part is brought into line with the figure 9 on the 24 hour ring. It will be noted that the time is 4 a.m. in New York, and 2 p.m. at night in Bombay, as indicated by the darkened part of the 24-hour ring.

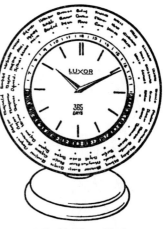

World Time Clock

Y

Year Clock   1685

The term refers to a clock which runs for one year with one winding. There are clocks which run for 400 DAYS (q.v.) with one winding and also ELECTRIC BATTERY Clocks (q.v.) which run for up to 7 years before renewal of the battery is necessary. But year clock refers to either a weight-driven or spring-driven clock fitted with the usual form of escapement, in other words, an ordinary clock but geared to run for 12 months.

Zaandam Clock

Thomas Tompion made a few bracket year clocks up to about 1700 and there are to be found both longcase and bracket clocks by other famous makers. In comparatively recent years longcase, weight-driven clocks have been made to run for 12 months. Some owners of the older year clocks have so arranged that the winding of the clock shall be the occasion of a party, and a book is preserved for the signature names of the winder. Famous names are to be discovered in some of these records.

Year clocks are also known as 'anniversary clocks'. (To be wound up once a year on a particular day.)

Such clocks, when spring- or weight-driven, i.e. not electric clocks, are rare. A Tompion year clock could be worth anything from £7,000 to £15,000, and an 18th century year clock £500 to £1,500. A 19th century clock would be worth about £250 to £500 or £600. In all instances the clocks could be worth more than the figures estimated.

Z
Zaandam Clock   1600

The earliest form of Dutch hanging clock. An elaborate type of LANTERN CLOCK (q.v.) fitted onto a bracket with the weights exposed.

The early Zaandam clocks were fitted with the VERGE ESCAPEMENT (q.v.) with FOLIOT (q.v.) and after 1656 with the pendulum.

At this period, the pendulum and the weights were exposed. After the introduction of the long seconds pendulum by William Clement in 1670, and the ANCHOR ESCAPEMENT, long pendulums were fitted to Zaandam clocks.

Value: £35 to, say, £200.

See also FRIESLAND CLOCK.

A Guide to Assess the Dates of

English Antique Clocks

The dates etc. given can only be approximate. There can be no hard and fast rule as there was much overlapping. As an instance; Thomas Tompion gave to the Pump Room, Bath in 1709 a long-case clock of mahogany, but mahogany became popular after 1730. Mahogany must have been known long before even 1709, and it is quite conceivable that the wood was imported from abroad especially.

The principle moulding under the hood of

Grandfather clocks—Convex before 1700.
    —Concave after 1700.

Curves to top of doors of grandfather clocks—after 1720.

Glass side panels on the hood of grandfather clocks indicate London made clocks.

Solid side panels on the hood of the grandfather clocks indicate provincial made clocks.

Square calendar apertures to dials indicate London made clocks.

Curved calendar apertures to dials indicate provincial made clocks.

Mahogany used for making clock cases introduced about 1730.

Portico top to grandfather and bracket clock case—from 1660.

Flat top to grandfather and bracket clock case—from 1670.

Domed top to grandfather and bracket clock case—from 1675.

Crested top to grandfather clock cases—from 1685.
    (introduced by Grinling Gibbons 1675–1680).

Basket top to bracket clock cases—1680.
    (introduced by Grinling Gibbons 1675–1680).

Double basket top to bracket clock cases—1700.

Inverted bell top, square dial bracket clock cases—1700.

113

Inverted bell top, arched dial bracket clock cases—1720.

Bell top, ebony veneer, square dial clock cases—1700.

Bell top, mahogany, clock cases—1730.

Arched hood to grandfather clock cases—1720.

Broken arch to grandfather clock cases—1720.

Broken arch hood to grandfather clock cases—1760.

Square brass dial grandfather and bracket clocks—before 1720.

Arched brass dial grandfather and bracket clocks—after 1720.

Painted dials, grandfather and bracket clocks—after 1750.

Silvered dials, no spandrels, grandfather and bracket clocks—after 1760.

Round dials, grandfather and bracket clocks—1785. (introduced by Ellicott)

Broken arch dial to grandfather and bracket clocks—after 1795.

Name of maker at bottom of dial plate—from 1670.

Name on chapter ring of dial—from 1690.

Quarter hour divisions only on lantern clock dial (usually hour hand only)—from 1600.

Quarter and minute divisions on grandfather and bracket clocks—before 1720.

Minute divisions only on grandfather and bracket clocks—after 1720.

Seconds hand on grandfather clock—after 1675.

Seconds hand on bracket clock—after 1795.

A Guide to Tompion Clocks

Thomas Tompion numbered the majority of his clocks.

Some special clocks such as the year clocks, Royal clocks and clocks made previous to *circa* 1685 were not numbered.

Tompion must have made a large number of lantern clocks, what may be called every-day clocks, that were not numbered with the same size punch; a smaller size numbered punch was used.

It is interesting to note that relatively few lantern clocks survive. This could well be because they wore out and were then discarded and also because they were 30 hour clocks and were not considered important as furnishing items.

Tompion started to number clocks *circa* 1685. The numbering is in the form of a punch mark with arabic block figure type—not engraved—usually positioned at the base of the back plate just behind the pendulum bob on bracket clocks, and at the base of the back plate on longcase clocks. On at least two clocks the same number appears. See No. 85 in the chart of numbers.

Sometimes a similar number to the one stamped on the movement is to be found on the top or side rails of the back door of bracket clocks and on the top or side of the waist door of longcase clocks.

The tables and charts have been compiled over the last 40 years. Many of the clocks have passed through the author's hands. Numbers have also been 'collected' from books, magazine articles, auction sale catalogues, and dealers' advertisements. Rarely during the past few years has a fresh number come to light.

There is evidence that Tompion numbered a quantity of clocks at the same time because occasionally one comes across a clock with a number suggesting a date where obviously the clock was finished at a later date. Even so, such instances are few and far between and cannot affect the usefulness of the guide chart when assessing the date of the clock.

The Reign of Thomas Tompion	
1671—1702-3	Thomas Tompion
1702—1709	Tompion and Banger
1709—1712	Thomas Tompion
1712—1713	Tompion and Graham
Thereafter to 1751	George Graham, when he, too, died.

Edward Banger was a nephew of Tompion and joined him *circa* 1702. They quarrelled and ceased to work together after 1709. Clocks made during partnership were signed *Tho: Tompion Edw: Banger*.

George Graham entered Tompion's service *circa* 1696 as a trained craftsman, and eventually married Tompion's niece. From 1712 to Tompion's death in 1713, he was in partnership with Tompion and clocks were signed *Thomas Tompion and George Graham*. After Tompion's death, Graham took over the business and thereafter his name only appears.

Excluding special clocks, pre-numbering and lantern clocks, Tompion made about 600 clocks.

The chart which follows will, it is hoped, form a useful guide when assessing the age of a Tompion clock. Nearly 200 clocks have been accounted for in this list and spaces are left for the reader to fill in fresh clocks as they come to light.

Collecting Tompion numbers can be interesting and rewarding.

A guide to assessing the age of Tompion Clocks

Clocks signed by Tompion
Number

1. 1685

2. 1685

3. 1685 Bracket strike clock with pull repeat on two bells. Seen at the British Clockmakers Heritage Exhibition, 1952.

4. 1685

5. 1685

6. 1685 Bracket strike clock with pull repeat.

7. 1685 Small size bracket strike clock with pull quarter repeat (See R. W. Symonds 'Thomas Tompion', Fig. 112).

Clocks signed by Tompion
Number

8. 1685 Bracket timepiece with pull quarter repeat.

9. 1685

10. 1685

11. 1685 Bracket strike clock with pull repeat.

12. 1685

13. 1685

14. 1685 Longcase one month clock (See R. W. Symonds 'Thomas Tompion', Fig. 54).

15. 1685 Small bracket strike clock with pull quarter repeat.

16. 1685 Bracket strike clock with ting-tang quarters (See R. W. Symond's 'Thomas Tompion', Fig. 113).

17. 1685 Bracket strike clock with pull quarter repeat. Bequeathed to St. Bartholmew's Hospital.

18. 1685

19. 1685

20. 1685

21. 1686

22. 1686 Bracket timepiece with five minute repeat.

23. 1686

24. 1686

25. 1686

26. 1686

27. 1686 Longcase one month clock, in olivewood, and walnut marquetry case.

28. 1686

29. 1686

30. 1686

31. 1686

32. 1686

33. 1686

34. 1686

35. 1686 Bracket clock with strike and pull repeat. To be seen in the Victoria & Albert Museum, London.

36. 1686 Longcase clock in walnut.

37. 1686 Bracket strike clock with pull repeat.

38. 1686 Bracket strike clock with pull repeat.

39. 1686

40. 1687

41. 1687

42. 1687 Bracket timepiece with pull quarter repeat. (See R. W. Symond's 'Thomas Tompion', Fig. 114).

43. 1687

44. 1687

E

45. 1687

46. 1687

47. 1687

48. 1687

49. 1687

50. 1687

51. 1687 Small timepiece with pull quarter repeat. (See R. W. Symond's 'Thomas Tompion', Fig. 116).

52. 1687

53. 1687

54. 1687

55. 1687 Small timepiece with pull quarter repeat. Similar to number 51.

56. 1687 Bracket strike clock with pull repeat.

57. 1687

58. 1687

59. 1687

60. 1688

61. 1688

62. 1688

63. 1688

64. 1688 Longcase one month clock in walnut.

65. 1688

66. 1688 Bracket timepiece with pull quarter repeat. (See R. W. Symond's 'Thomas Tompion', Fig. 118).

67. 1688

68. 1688

69. 1688 Longcase one month clock (Mentioned in Ullyett's 'In Quest of Clocks', page 21. Also Cescincky's 'Old English Master Clockmakers', Figs. 70 and 71).

70. 1688

71. 1688

72. 1688

73. 1688

74. 1688 Bracket timepiece with pull quarter repeat. (See F. H. Green's book 'Old English Clocks', Plate X.)

75. 1688

76. 1688

77. 1688 Bracket timepiece with pull quarter repeat.

78. 1688 Bracket timepiece with pull quarter repeat.

79. 1688 Dural escapement clock. To be seen in the Hessische Landes Museum, Cassel. (See *Antiquarian Horology*, March 1958.)

80. 1689

81. 1689 Longcase clock in walnut.

82. 1689

83. 1689

84. 1689

85. 1689 Bracket timepiece with alarm and pull quarter repeat. (See F. H Green's Old English Clocks'. Plate XIV. Also Ullyett's 'In Quest of Clocks', page 84.) Sold at Sotheby's January 30, 1964. F. H. Green records there are two No. 85 clocks. Clock No. 271 is named

Tompion and Banger and 272 is named Graham, which indicates that some plates were numbered and used at a later date.

86. 1869 Bracket strike clock with pull repeat.

87. 1689 Bracket pull quarter clock. Sold at Sotheby's, December 5, 1958

88. 1689 Bracket timepiece with

pull quarter repeat. Said to be the only walnut bracket clock by Tompion. (See R. W. Symond's 'Thomas Tompion', Fig. 119.)

89. 1689 Bracket timepiece with pull repeat. (See R. W Symond's 'Thomas Tompion', Fig. 115.)

90. 1689

91. 1689

92. 1689 Bracket strike clock with repeat. Signed 'Tompion and Banger'. An instance where plates numbered were not used at the time. Sold at Christie's, March 21, 1957.

93. 1689 Bracket timepiece in rosewood case, with pull quarter repeat. Sold at Sotheby's, November 17, 1950, and again at Sotheby's, March 1, 1963.

94. 1689

95. 1689 Bracket strike clock with pull repeat. Sold at Sotheby's, June 8, 1962.

96. 1689 Bracket timepiece with pull quarter repeat. (See Ullyett's 'In Quest of Clocks', Page 154. Also F. H. Green's 'Old English Clocks', Plates XXIV and XXV.)

97. 1689

98. 1689 Bracket strike clock with pull quarter repeat.

99. 1689 Bracket strike clock with pull quarter repeat. At Exhibition of English Clocks 1600–1850, Temple Newsam House, Leeds, September, 1949.

100. 1690

101. 1690

102. 1690

103. 1690 Bracket strike clock in walnut case. Sold at Sotheby's, December 10, 1964.

104. 1690

105. 1690

106. 1690 Longcase one month clock in walnut. Sold at Sotheby's, May 13, 1960.

107. 1690

108. 1690 Bracket timepiece with pull quarter repeat.

109. 1690

110. 1690

111. 1690

112. 1690

113. 1690

114. 1690

115. 1691 Longcase clock in walnut.

116. 1691

117. 1691

118. 1691

119. 1691

120. 1691

121. 1691

122. 1691

123. 1691

124. 1691

125. 1691

126. 1691

127. 1691

128. 1691

129. 1691

130. 1691 Longcase clock.

131. 1691 Longcase clock in burr walnut with three train grand sonnerie striking. (See R. W. Symond's 'Thomas Tompion', Fig. 55. Also F. H. Green's 'Old English Clocks', Plates XV and XVI.)

132. 1691 Black Longcase three-month clock. To be seen in Ilbert collection, British Museum.

(See R. W. Symond's Penguin book, 'Tompion'. Also F. H. Green's 'Old English Clocks', Plates XVII, XVIII, and XXXVII.) Sold at Christie's, November 1958.

133. 1691

134. 1691

135. 1691

136. 1691 Longcase clock.

137. 1691

138. 1691

139. 1691

140. 1692 Longcase one month clock in walnut (*Apollo* advertisement, December 1948.)

141. 1692

142. 1692

143. 1692

144. 1692

145. 1692

146. 1692

147. 1692

148. 1692

149. 1692

150. 1692

151. 1692

152

153. 1692

154. 1692

155. 1692

156. 1692

157. 1692   Longcase clock in walnut. Sold at Sotheby's, February 22, 1952.

158. 1692

159. 1692

160. 1693

161. 1693   Black bracket strike clock with pull quarter repeat. Tic-tac escapement. (See R. W. Symond's 'Thomas Tompion', Fig. 124.)

162. 1693   Longcase clock in walnut. Sold at Sotheby's, March 5, 1963. Formerly in the Wetherfield Collection.

163. 1693

164. 1693

165. 1693

166. 1693

167. 1693   Black bracket strike clock. (See Mallett's of Bond St. catalogue, 1933.)

168. 1693

169. 1693

170. 1693

171. 1693   Bracket strike clock with pull quarter repeat. (See R. W. Symond's 'Thomas Tompion', Fig. 125. See Mallett's of Bond St. catalogue.) Sold at Christie's, 1938.

172. 1693

173. 1693

174. 1693

175. 1693

176. 1693

177. 1693

178. 1693 Bracket strike clock with pull repeat. (See F. H. Green's 'Old English Clocks', Plate XXXII and XXXIII. Also Cescinsky's 'Old English Master Clock Makers', Figs. 191 and 192.)

179. 1693

180. 1694 Bracket strike clock with pull repeat.

181. 1694 Bracket strike clock with pull repeat. (Advertisement, Biggs of Maidenhead, June 1957.)

182. 1694 Bracket strike clock with pull repeat. Sold at Sotheby's, July 1947.

183. 1694

184. 1694 Bracket strike clock with pull repeat.

185. 1694 Longcase clock in marquetry.

186. 1694

187. 1694 Bracket one-month strike clock with pull repeat. Sold at Christie's, May 7, 1953.

188. 1694

189. 1694

190. 1694

191. 1694

192. 1694

193. 1694

194. 1694 Bracket strike clock with pull quarter repeat. Sold at Sotheby's, September 8, 1948.

195. 1694 Bracket strike clock with pull quarter repeat. Sold at Sotheby's, January 30, 1964

196. 1694 Bracket clock with grande sonnerie strike (See F. H. Green's 'Old English Clocks'.)

197. 1694

198. 1694 Bracket strike clock with pull quarter repeat. Sold at Sotheby's, December 13, 1963.

199. 1694 Bracket strike clock with pull quarter repeat. (See catalogue of Internation Art Exhibition, Plate 129, 1962.) Clock can be seen in the V. & A. Museum, London.

200. 1695

201. 1695 Bracket strike clock
with pull quarter re-
peat.

202. 1695 Bracket strike clock
with pull quarter re-
peat. Sold at Sothe-
by's, October 119,
1954.

203. 1695 Bracket strike clock
with pull quarter re-
peat. Sold at Sothe-
by's, June 8, 1962.

204. 1695 Bracket strike clock
with pull quarter re-
peat. (Percy Webster
advertisement.)

205. 1695

206. 1695

207. 1695

208. 1695 Longcase clock. Sold
at Sotheby's, May 20,
1949, and again at
Sotheby's, May 13,
1966.

209. 1695

210. 1695

211. 1965

212. 1695 Bracket strike clock
with pull quarter re-
peat. (See R. W. Sy-
mond's 'Thomas Tom-
pion', Fig. 121.)

213. 1695

214. 1695

215. 1695

216. 1695

217. 1695 Bracket clock with
three-train grande son-
nerie strike. (See R.
W. Symond's 'Tho-
mas Tompion', Fig.
141.)

218. 1695

219. 1695

220. 1696 Bracket strike clock
with pull quarter re-
peat. (See R. W. Sy-
mond's 'Thomas Tom-
pion', Fig. 120.)

221. 1696

222. 1696 Miniature bracket
clock with pull quar-
ter repeat, $4\frac{1}{2}$ in. high.
Formerly in the Ilbert
Collection. Original
case found and bought
by Ilbert at Sotheby's.
(See R. W. Symond's

'Thomas Tompion',
Figs. 145 and 146.
Also Ullyett's 'In
Quest of Clocks', page
8.)

223. 1696

224. 1696 Small bracket strike
clock with pull quar-
ter repeat.

225. 1696 Small bracket clock
with pull quarter re-
peat. (At Antique
Dealers, Fair, London,
1951.)

226. 1696 Bracket strike clock
with pull quarter re-
peat. (Article in *Ap-
ollo*, March 1952.)
Sold at Christie's, July
26, 1951.

227. 1696

228. 1696 Bracket strike clock
with pull quarter re-
peat.

229. 1696

230. 1696

231. 1696 Longcase clock in walnut. (See *Antiquarian
Horology*, September
1965.)

232. 1696

233. 1696

234. 1696

235. 1696 Small bracket strike
clock with pull quar-
ter repeat, 9in. high.

236. 1696

237. 1696

238. 1696

239. 1696

240. 1697 Bracket strike clock
with pull quarter re-
peat. (See F. H.
Green's 'Old English
Clocks' Plates XXXIV
and XXXV.) Sold at
Sotheby's, March 25,
1949.

241. 1697

242. 1697 Longcase clock in walnut. (Percy Webster
advertisement, 1948.)

243. 1697 Bracket strike clock
with pull quarter re-
peat. Sold at Chris-
tie's, December 12,
1946, and also at So-
theby's, November 10,
1965.

244. 1697 Bracket strike clock
with pull quarter re-
peat.

245. 1697

246. 1697

247. 1697

248. 1697

249. 1697 Bracket strike clock
with pull quarter re-
peat. Shown at the
British Clockmakers
Heritage Exhibition,
1952. Catalogue No.
129.

250. 1697

251. 1697 Longcase one-month
clock with repeating
mechanism, in wal-
nut. (See R. W. Sy-
mond's 'Thomas Tom-
pion', Figs. 75 and
76.)

252. 1697 Bracket strike clock
with pull quarter re-
peat. Signed 'Tom-
pion and Banger'. An
instance where the
movement was not
made until at least
1702.

253. 1697

254. 1697

254. 1697 Longcase clock. Now
in an oak case.

255. 1697 Bracket strike and alarm clock with pull
quarter repeat.

256. 1697

257. 1697

258. 1697

259.

260. 1698 Bracket strike clock
with pull quarter re-
peat. Exhibited at the
British Clockmakers
Heritage Exhibition,
1952, Catalogue No.
121. Sold at Sotheby's,
February 25, 1949.
Also at Sotheby's,
March 6, 1954.

261. 1698 Bracket strike clock
with pull quarter re-
peat.

262. 1698

263. 1698

264. 1698

265. 1698

266. 1698

267. 1698 Bracket strike clock
with pull quarter re-
peat. (Biggs of Maid-
enhead advertisement
in *Antiquarian Horology*,
September 1964.)

268. 1698

269. 1698

270. 1698

271. 1698 Bracket strike clock and pull quarter repeat.

272. 1698 Bracket strike clock with pull quarter repeat. Sold at Sotheby's, December 2, 1966.

273. 1698 Bracket one month, strike clock with pull repeat. British Clockmakers Heritage Exhibition 1952. Catalogue No. 131. (See R. W. Symond's 'Thomas Tompion', Fig. 128.)

274. 1698

275. 1698

276. 1698 Bracket strike clock with pull quarter repeat. Sold at Sotheby's, July 26, 1935.

277. 1698

278. 1698

279. 1698

280. 1699

281. 1699

282. 1699 Small bracket strike clock with pull quarter repeat.

283. 1699

284. 1699 Walnut one month longcase clock. Sold at Sotheby's, June 30, 1950.

285. 1699 Miniature bracket strike clock with pull quarter repeat. (See R. W. Symond's 'Thomas Tompion', Fig. 126.)

286. 1699 Bracket strike clock with pull quarter repeat. (See R. W. Symond's 'Thomas Tompion', Figs. 127, 165, 190, 218, and 236.)

287. 1699 Bracket strike clock with pull quarter repeat. Sold at Sotheby's, December 13, 1963.)

288. 1699 One-month longcase clock in walnut. (See F. H. Green's 'Old English Clocks', Plate XIX and XX.)

289. 1699

290. 1699

291. 1699 Bracket clock with three-train grande sonnerie strike.

292. 1699 Longcase one-month clock, in walnut. (See Cescinsky's 'Old English Master Clockmakers', Page 58. And Ullyett's 'In Quest of Clocks', Page 21. And R. W. Symond's 'Thomas Tompion', Figs. 38 and 39.)

293. 1699

294. 1699

295. 1699

296. 1699 Longcase one month clock in walnut. (See R. W. Symond's 'Thomas Tompion', Figs. 38, 39, 57, and 79.)

297. 1699

298. 1699 Bracket strike clock with pull quarter repeat. (See R. W. Symond's 'Tompion', Figs. 122 and 123. Also Cescinsky's 'Old English Master Clockmakers', Page 128.)

299. 1699

300. 1699 Large bracket clock with three-train grand sonnerie strike. (See R. W. Symond's 'Thomas Tompion', Figs. 129, 185, and 215. Also an article by *Antiquarian Horology*, R. K. Foulkes in March 1959.)

301. 1699 Longcase one month clock in walnut (See Cescinksy's 'Old English Master Clockmakers', Page 59.)

302. 1699 Longcase one month clock, in walnut. (See R. W. Symond's 'Thomas Tompion', Figs. 42, 43, 60 and 89.) This clock is signed Tompion and Banger'.

303. 1699

304. 1700

305. 1700 Longcase one month clock, in walnut. Sold at Sotheby's June 23, 1961.

306. 1700 Longcase one month clock, in walnut. Sold at Sotheby's, December 10, 1954, and Sotheby's, December 16, 1955.

Clocks signed by Tompion
Number

307. 1700

308. 1700

309. 1700

310. 1700

311. 1700

312. 1700 Bracket strike clock with pull quarter repeat. (See Allan Lloyd's 'Chats on Old Clocks', Plate 19.)

313. 1700

314. 1700

315. 1700

316. 1700 Longcase clock, in walnut.

317. 1700

318. 1700

319. 1700

320. 1701

321. 1701 Longcase one-month clock, in walnut and mulberry. (See F. H. Green's 'Old English Clocks', Plate XXI and XXII.)

Clocks signed by Tompion
Number

322. 1701

323. 1701

324. 1701

325. 1701 Longcase one-month clock, in walnut. Shown at Antique Dealers Fair, 1950.

326. 1701

327. 1701 Longcase one-month clock, in walnut.

328. 1701 Bracket strike clock with pull quarter repeat. (See *Antique Collector*, July 1943, and Cescinsky's 'Old English Master Clockmakers', Page 129.)

329. 1701

330. 1701

331. 1701

332. 1701

333. 1701

334. 1701

336. 1701 Longcase one-month clock, in walnut. Sold at Sotheby's, February 14, 1958.

Clocks signed by Tompion
Number

337. 1701

338. 1701

339. 1702

340. 1702

341. 1702

342. 1702

343. 1702 Longcase clock in dark oak. (The Wetherfield Collection catalogue, Fig. 70, Page 60.) Sold at Sotheby's, May 16, 1964.

344. 1702

345. 1702

346. 1702

347. 1702

348. 1702

349. 1702

Clocks signed by Tompion and Banger
Number

350. 1702

351. 1702 Ebonized longcase clock. (See R. W. Symond's 'Thomas Tompion', Fig. 44 and 45. And Cescinsky's 'Old English Master Clockmakers', Page 61 Fig. 80, states 'oak case, veneered ebony'.

Clocks signed by Tompion and Banger
Number

352. 1702

353. 1702

354. 1702

356. 1702

357. 1702 Longcase clock in marquetry and walnut. Sold at Sotheby's, November 23, 1953.

358. 1702

359. 1702 Longcase clock.

360. 1703 Longcase clock, in walnut. Signed 'Thos. Tompion'. (See R. W. Symond's 'Thomas Tompion', Fig. 58 of dial only.)

361. 1703

362. 1703

363. 1703 Longcase clock.

364. 1703

365. 1703 Longcase one-month clock, in walnut.

366. 1703

367. 1703

368. 1703 Ebony veneered bracket clock with pull quarter on six bells. (Watkin's advertisement *Connoisseur*, April 1933.)

369. 1703

370. 1703

371. 1703 Longcase clock, in mulberry veneer. Signed 'Tompion'. (See R. W. Symond's 'Thomas Tompion', Figs. 40, 41, and 59. Also Cescinsky's 'Old English Clockmakers', Figs. 78 and 79.)

372. 1703

373. 1703

374. 1703

375. 1703 Bracket strike clock with pull quarter repeat.

376. 1703 Bracket strike clock with pull quarter repeat.

377. 1703

378. 1703

379. 1703

380. 1704 Longcase clock, in walnut. Sold at Sotheby's, February 13, 1948.

381. 1704

382. 1704

383. 1704

384. 1704 Longcase clock, in walnut. Shown at the Antique Dealers Fair, 1956.

385. 1704

386. 1704

387. 1704

388. 1704 Bracket strike clock with pull quarter. Now in Windsor Castle. (See R. W. Symond's 'Thomas Tompion', Page 155, Fig. B.)

389. 1704

390. 1704 Bracket strike clock with pull quarter repeat. Similar to clock No. 249.

391. 1704 Bracket strike clock with pull quarter repeat. Signed 'Thos. Tompion'.

392. 1704 Thirty-hour wall timepiece, in mahogany
case. Sold at Sotheby's
December 11, 1953.

393. 1704

394. 1704

395. 1704 Longcase one-month
clock.

396. 1704

397. 1704

398. 1704

399. 1704

400. 1705

401. 1705

402. 1705

403. 1705 Bracket strike clock
with pull quarter re-
peat.

404. 1705 Bracket strike clock
with pull quarter re-
peat. Strikes the suc-
ceeding hour at the
$\frac{1}{2}$ hour (Dutch striking.) (See Ullyett's
'In Quest of Clocks',
Plate XLVIII.)

405. 1705

406. 1705 Bracket strike clock
with pull quarter re-
peat.

407. 1705

408. 1705

409. 1705

410. 1705

411. 1705 Bracket strike clock
with pull quarter re-
peat.

412. 1705

413. 1705

414. 1705 Bracket strike clock
with pull quarter re-
peat. (See R. W. Sy-
mond's 'Thomas Tom-
pion', Figs. 105 and
145.)

415. 1705

416. 1705

417. 1705

418. 1705 Bracket strike clock
with pull quarter re-
peat. (See R. W. Sy-
mond's 'Thomas Tom-
pion', Figs. 131, 150,
and 192. Also Ces-
cinsky's 'Old English
clockmakers', Figs.
197, and 198.)

419. 1705 Thirty hour wall alarm clock, in walnut. (See R. W. Symond's 'Thomas Tompion', Figs. 96, 99, and 100.)

420. 1706 Bracket strike clock with pull quarter repeat. Strikes succeeding hour at $\frac{1}{2}$ hour (Dutch striking.) Sold at Sotheby's, July 14, 1961.

421. 1706

422. 1706 Clock with grand sonnerie strike, in tortoiseshell case. (See R. W. Symond's 'Thomas Tompion', Figs. 140, 163, 194, and 235.)

423. 1706

424. 1706 Bracket strike clock with pull quarter repeat. (See R. W. Symond's 'Thomas Tompion' Figs. 133, 197, 217 and 237.)

425. 1706 Bracket strike clock with pull quarter repeat. Signed 'Tompion', only. Sold at Sotheby's, July 18, 1952.

426. 1706

427. 1706

428. 1706

429. 1706 Bracket strike clock with pull quarter repeat.

430. 1706

431. 1706

432. 1706 Bracket strike clock with pull quarter repeat. (Webster advertisement *Apollo*, June 1947.) Sold at Sotheby's, May 13, 1966.

433. 1706

434. 1706 Lantern alarm clock. (See R. W. Symond's 'Thomas Tompion', Fig. 98a.)

435. 1706

436. 1706 Bracket clock with grand sonnerie strike, in tortoiseshell case. (See R. W. Symond's 'Thomas Tompion', Plate IV and Figs. 149, 162, 193, and 216.)

437. 1706

438. 1706 Bracket strike clock with pull quarter repeat.

Clocks signed by Tompion and Banger
Number

439. 1706

440. 1707 Bracket strike clock with pull quarter repeat. Sold at Sotheby's, October 28, 1932.

441. 1707 Bracket strike clock with pull quarter repeat. Sold at Sotheby's, May 20, 1949.

442. 1707

443. 1707 Bracket clock with grand sonnerie strike. Sold at Sotheby's, May 27, 1954.

444. 1707 Bracket strike clock with pull quarter repeat. Sold at Sotheby's, September 30, 1953.

445. 1707 Bracket strike clock with pull quarter repeat. Sold at Sotheby's, May 7, 1963.

446. 1707

447. 1707

448. 1707

449. 1707

450. 1707 Bracket strike clock with pull quarter repeat.

Clocks signed by Tompion
Number

451. 1707

452. 1707

453. 1707

454. 1707 Bracket strike clock with pull quarter repeat. Sold at Sotheby's, February 1, 1963

455. 1707

456. 1707

457. 1707 Miniature bracket strike clock with pull quarter repeat. Seen at Antique Dealers Fair, 1948. (See R. W. Symond's 'Thomas Tompion', Fig. 198.)

458. 1707 Bracket strike clock with pull quarter repeat.

459. 1707 Bracket strike clock with pull quarter repeat. Sold at Christie's March 16, 1967.

460. 1708 Small bracket strike clock with pull quarter repeat. Silver mounts. Known as the 'Barnard Clock'. (See R. W. Symond's 'Thomas Tompion', Figs. 142, 144, 143, and 199.)

461. 1708 Small bracket strike clock with pull quarter repeat. Sold at Sotheby's December 10, 1964.

462. 1708

463. 1708 Bracket clock with grande sonnerie strike. (See R. W. Symond's 'Thomas Tompion', Fig. 195.)

464. 1708

465. 1708

466. 1708

467. 1708

468. 1708

469. 1708

470. 1708

471. 1708

472. 1708

473. 1708

474. 1708 Bracket strike clock with pull quarter repeat. Sold at Christies, May 16, 1946.

475. 1708 Bracket strike clock with pull quarter repeat. Shown at Temple Newsam House Exhibition, Leicester, September 1949. Catalogue quotes 'Last clock made by Tompion and Banger'.

Clocks signed by Tompion
Number

476. 1708

477. 1708 Bracket clock with grande sonnerie strike (See R. W. Symond's 'Thomas Tompion', Figs. 130, 164, 196, and 234.)

478. 1708 Longcase clock, in burr walnut. Signed 'Tompion and Banger'. Sold at Sotheby's, October 28, 1963.

479. 1708 Bracket strike clock with pull quarter repeat. Sold at Christie's, October 27, 1916.

480. 1709 Longcase clock, in walnut. Sold at Sotheby's, June 23, 1961, and at Sotheby's, December 1, 1961.

481. 1709

482. 1709

483. 1709

484. 1709

485. 1709 Longcase clock, in walnut. Offered at Sotheby's July, 8, 1949.

486. 1709

487. 1709 Bracket one-month strike clock with pull quarter repeat.

488. 1709 Bracket clock with grande sonnerie strike. Signed 'Geo. Graham'

489. 1709

490. 1709

491. 1709

492. 1709

493. 1709

494. 1709

495. 1709

496. 1709 Ebonised longcase clock. Signed 'Tompion and Banger. Sold at Sotheby's, November 9, 1956.

497. 1709

498. 1709

499. 1709

500. 1710

501. 1710

502. 1710

503. 1710

504. 1710 Longcase clock, in ebony veneer. (See Cescinsky's 'Old English Clockmakers', Page 63. Figs. 84, and 85.)

505. 1710

506. 1710

507. 1710

508. 1710

509. 1710

510. 1710

511. 1710

512. 1710

513. 1710

514. 1710

515. 1710

516. 1710

517. 1710

518. 1710 Thirty-hour lantern alarm clock. (See R. W. Symond's 'Thomas Tompion', Fig. 98.) This clock is now in the British Museum, London.

519. 1710

520. 1711

521. 1711

522. 1711

523. 1711

524. 1711

525. 1711

526. 1711 Bracket strike clock with pull quarter repeat. Signed 'Geo. Graham'. (Illustrated in the *Connoisseur*, March 1945.)

527. 1711

528. 1711

529. 1711

530. 1711

531. 1711 Longcase clock, in ebony veneer. (See Ullyett's 'In Quest of Clocks', Page 172.)

532. 1711

533. 1711 Longcase clock, in ebony veneer. (See F. H. Green's 'Old English Clocks', Plate XXIII.)

534. 1711 Longcase one-month clock, in ebony veneer. (See Ullyett's 'In Quest of Clocks.')

535. 1711

536. 1711

537. 1711 Bracket strike clock with pull quarter repeat. (See R. W. Symond's 'Thomas Tompion', Figs. 134, and 200.)

538. 1711

539. 1711

540. 1711 Ebonised longcase clock. Sold at Sotheby's, April 8, 1960, and also, May 7, 1963.

541. 1712

542. 1712 Longcase clock, in walnut. (See F. H. Green's 'Old English Clocks', Plate XXXVII.)

543. 1712

544. 1712

545. 1712 Bracket strike clock with pull quarter repeat.

546. 1712

547. 1712

548. 1712

549. 1712

550. 1712

551. 1712

552. 1712

553. 1712

554. 1712

555. 1712

556. 1712 Longcase clock, in olive wood. (See *Horological Journal*, December, 1953.)

557. 1712 Bracket strike clock and pull quarter repeat. Signed 'Geo. Graham'.

558. 1712

559. 1712

560. 1713

561. 1713

562. 1713

563. 1713

564. 1713

565. 1713

566. 1713

567. 1713

568. 1713

569. 1713

570. 1713

571. 1713

572. 1713 Brass lantern clock with short pendulum and alarm.

573. 1713

574. 1713

575. 1713

576. 1713

577. 1713

578. 1713

579. 1713

580. 1714

Numbers which follow 580 are signed 'Geo. Graham'.

Crowned Heads of England

Date	King or Queen	Length of Reign	Year of Death	House	Remarks
1189	Richard I	Sept. April	1199		
1199	John	May Oct.	1216		
1216	Henry III	Oct. Nov.	1272	Plantagenet	
1272	Edward I	Nov. July	1307		
1307	Edward II	July Jan.	1327		Dethroned. Murdered
1327	Edward III	Jan. June	1377		
1377	Richard II	June Sept.	1400		Dethroned 1399. Murdered
1399	Henry IV	Sept. Mar.	1413	Lancaster	
1413	Henry V	Mar. Aug.	1422		
1422	Henry VI	Sept. June	1471		Deposed 1461
1461	Edward IV		1483	York	
1483	Edward V		1483		Deposed
1483	Richard III	June Aug.	1485		Slain at Bosworth
1485	Henry VII	Aug. Apr.	1509		
1509	Henry VIII	Apr. Jan.	1547		
1547	Edward VI		1553	Tudor	
1553	Jane	July	1554		Beheaded
1553	Mary	July Nov.	1558		
1558	Elizabeth I	Mar.	1603		

Date	King or Queen	Length of Reign		Year of Death	House	Remarks
1603	James I		Mar.	1625		James VI of Scotland
1625	Charles I		Jan.	1649		Beheaded
1649	Commonwealth		Sept.	1658	Stuart	Oliver Cromwell Protector 1653 Richard Cromwell Protector 1658 Resigned 1659
1660	Charles II	May	Feb.	1685		
1685	James II		Aug.	1701		Abdicated 1688
1689	William III (Prince of Orange) William and Mary		Feb.	1702		Mary died 1694
1702	Anne	Mar.	Aug.	1714		
1714	George I	Aug.	June	1727		
1727	George II	June	Oct.	1760		
1760	George III	Oct.	Jan.	1820	Hanover	
1820	George IV	Jan.	June	1830		
1830	William IV	June	June	1837		
1837	Victoria	June		1900		
1901	Edward VII			1909		
1910	George V			1935	Windsor	
1936	Edward VIII					Abdicated 1936
1937	George VI			1952		
1952	Elizabeth II					

DATES OF ACCESSION OF FRENCH KINGS, from 1498
and FRENCH CLOCK STYLES

1498—Louis XII

1515—François I

1547—Henri II

1559—François II

1560—Charles IX

1574—Henri III

1589—Henri IV — Baroque style.

1610—Louis XIII — Change from baroque of Henri IV to classic grandeur of Louis XIV beginning of use of scroll and shell-like forms.

1653—Louis XIV — Classic formality at the beginning with lavish modifications. Curved headed panels. Shell-work at top. Interlaced acanthus scrolls, André Charles Boulle introduces new style. Beginning of ormulu.

1715—Louis XV — Réference. Growing love of curves. Use of ormulu increases. Chinese influence.

1774—Louis XVI (Guillotined in 1793.) — Return to classic of Louis XIV but more delicate.

1792—*French Revolution— Republic* proclaimed

1804—*First Empire—* Napoleon I, Emperor — Empire: Neo-classic. Increased use of bronze appliqué and Vernis Martin Guillaume Martin (died 1745), Simon, Etienne, Julien, and Robert (1706–65). Did not invent but perfected the Vernis process. At the height of their fame had three factories in Paris, one of which was still in existence in 1785.

1814—Louis XVIII

1824—Charles X

1830—Louise-Philippe I

1848—*Second Republic*

1852—*Second Empire—* Napoleon III, Emperor.

1870—*Third Republic*

DIRECTOIRE   Transitional between Louis XVI (restrained classic) and Empire (Roman heavy).

EMPIRE   (1799–1814) Neo-classic. Increased use of bronze appliqué ornament. Continued with modification till 1840.

Vernis Martinc   A form of varnish introduced by the Martin brothers pre French polish.

BOULLE   André Charles (1642–1732). A cabinet maker, not the inventor of the Boulle style of tortoiseshell inlaid with brass etc. but the past master of the art, improving on the Renaissance artists.

ORMOLU   An alloy of copper and zinc and at times tin. Colour heightened by use of 'gold lacquer'.

NOTES—(1) Note that *Louis XVII* is missing—as son of Louis XVI he would have been heir to the throne, but he was imprisoned during the Revolution, died in prison in 1795, and never reigned.

(2) Note that *Napoleon II* is also missing. He was son of Napoleon I, born in 1811, after Napoleon I's second abdication he was recognized as emperor but in fact never assumed power (he was only four years old at the time).

Bibliography

Baillie, G. A. 'Watchmakers and Clockmakers of the World'.

Britten, F. J. (Revised by Baillie, Ilbert, and Clutton) 'Old Clocks and Watches and their Makers'.

Bruton, Eric, 'Dictionary of Clocks and Watches'. 'The Longcase Clock', 'Clocks and Watches 1400–1900'.

Chamberlain, Paul, 'It's about Time'.

de Carle, D. 'British Time' 'The Watch and Clockmakers Encyclopaedia'.

Hope-Jones, F. 'Electrical Timekeeping'.

Lloyd, Allen, H. 'The Collector's Dictionary of Clocks'.

Milham, Prof. Willis I. 'Time and Timekeepers'.

Robertson, J. Drummond 'The Evolution of Clockwork'.

Salomons, Sir David 'Breguet'.

Symonds, R. W. 'Thomas Tompion'

Tardy, 'La Pendule Francaise'.

Lee, Ronald, A. 'The Knibb Family Clockmakers'.

Hana, W. F. J. 'Friese Klokken', 'Klokken'.

The books enumerated are but a brief selection from about 2,000 books written on the subject of clocks and watches.